x
c.2

Balch, Glenn
Buck, wild

DATE DUE

MAR 3 0 79			
MAR 1 1 83			
OCT 1 4 '88			
JUL 31			
OCT 28 91			
APR 1 8 95			
MAY 7 2000			
MAY 3 0 2000			

BUCK, WILD

BUCK, WILD

By Glenn Balch

Illustrated by Ruth Sanderson

THOMAS Y. CROWELL
COMPANY
New York

By the Author:

The Brave Riders
Buck, Wild
The Flaxy Mare
Horse of Two Colors

Library of Congress Cataloging in Publication Data
Balch, Glenn, Buck, wild.
SUMMARY: Traces the first four years in the life of a wild mustang stallion with an unconquerable urge to be free.
1. Mustang—Legends and stories. [1. Mustang—Fiction. 2. Horses—Fiction] I. Sanderson, Ruth. II. Title.
PZ10.3.B183Bu   [Fic]   75-44168
                  ISBN 0-690-01055-9

2   3   4   5   6   7   8   9   10

X
C.2

To Dianne,
equestrienne

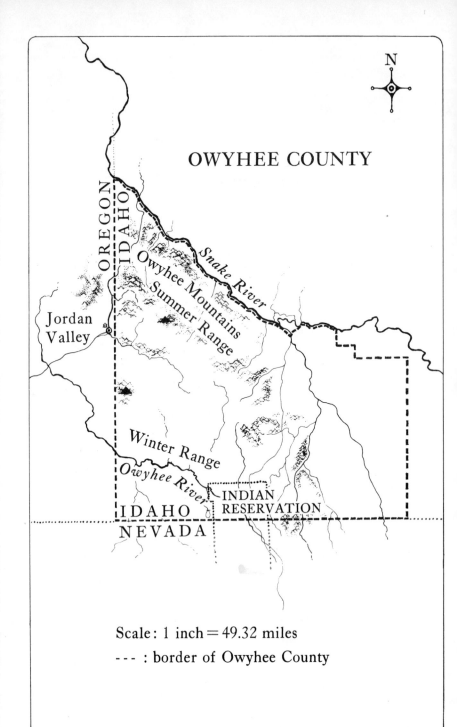

N

OWYHEE COUNTY

OREGON
IDAHO

Snake River

Owyhee Mountains
Summer Range

Jordan
Valley

Winter Range

Owyhee River

INDIAN
RESERVATION

IDAHO
NEVADA

Scale: 1 inch = 49.32 miles
--- : border of Owyhee County

1

It was written in centuries of wild existence that Buck should have a difficult life. When he was only a few days past a year old, his own father ran him out of the bunch, sent him fleeing into the sagebrush with a blood-dripping hip.

The mares of old Club's band dropped their new colts on the gravelly slopes of the rugged Owyhee mountain range in the early spring, when the hardy upland grasses were turning darker shades of green. Buck was one of the first to be born that year, long and angular and a washed-out yellow in color. After bumping down to the gritty earth, he immediately kicked and pawed a hole in the thin membrane of the birth sac and sucked in his first gulps of the crisp mountain air, without which he would have soon died. This first hazard overcome, he needed to rest and lie still a few seconds.

It was night, and not far away there was a big bulk, standing high in the gloom. It was Buck's mother who came nearer. Buck felt a soft and gentle touch. The mare found the opening in the membrane and helped slide it across Buck's shoulder and along his neck. Buck thrashed outward with his legs, gaining more freedom from the sac.

Buck knew at once that this big creature was very important to him. He knew he could give it his complete confidence and trust.

His mother was the only parent he would ever know. His father, Club, the old stallion, was out somewhere in the darkness, not even aware of his connection with Buck's birth. Club's duties of fatherhood and discipline were not to one but to the whole band.

But this was of no importance to the new foal. His mother was able to provide all the things he needed, including food and protection. Of course inherent strength and the will to live were necessary in his small body. Without that, nothing would save him. Indeed in nature's scheme of survival of the species he would not be worth saving.

The spark of life burned strong in Buck. He struck out vigorously with his legs, kicking the opening in the birth sac still wider. Something inside told him he had to get to his feet, to "stand," as horsemen put it. Up on four strong legs is the natural position for horses. Flight is their most reliable method of defense. Also the standing position is the one in which they take their food.

Buck rolled over on his thin chest, lifted his head, and pulled his front legs about. They were long and ungainly, with large knobs near their centers, but presently he got them to the front, with the knobs under the still damp long hairs of his chin. He strained against his forefeet, and the forepart of his lean bony shape began to rise from the ground. This, he felt, was a move in the right direction. He put on more pressure, and his shoulders and head lifted higher. Young foals are born with rough sandpaper-like soles on the bottoms of their feet to grip firmly whatever surface happens to be under them, to make it as certain as possible that they succeed in standing.

Buck's front feet did fine, but he had trouble with his hindquarters. They seemed to know what to do, but not just how to do it. In fact, his rear legs seemed to be hopelessly long and entangled. He tried to twist them around, so they would be under him, and finally did succeed but only partly, and then to his dismay, the effort upset the delicate balance in front. He felt himself falling. This alone was somewhat terrifying, but then he hit the earth with a solid thump that resulted in his first sensation of pain, a hurt to his pale pink little muzzle. He lay still a moment, blinking his eyes and not wishing to repeat the experience.

The mare then lowered her head and nuzzled him with gentle concern. Buck felt better. This large creature cared about him. The hurt to his nose was not so great. He wanted to stand up, as his mother did, to be closer to her. So he hitched his front legs around again, like a big ungainly crab. This time it was easier to get his knees under his chin, and his shoulders came up more readily. But those hind legs—they were so long and did not seem to be a part of him. They would not do what he wanted them to. He knew that in some way he had to get them under his body, and he made an effort, partly pulling them around and partly rolling over to be on top of them. But he rolled too far and went down on the other side, again falling hard. And again it was his chin that took the blow.

Buck gave up. That had been a tremendous effort, taking all his strength, and the only thing he had gained was another hurt. Letting his tired neck relax, he lay flat, dragging air deep into his small lungs. It was good to lie there in the gloom, with the big protective hulk of the mare looming against the dark sky above him. He felt safe. But only seconds passed before he lifted his neck and began hitching his long front legs around again. He had been born to live, not to die.

This time he was able to straighten his front legs entirely and raise himself until he was sitting on his haunches like a lean bony yellow dog. That encouraged him. Now all he had to do was get his hind legs in position. His muscles, young and inexperienced as they were, knew how to do it. He heaved himself upward. But his hind feet were still tangled in the birth sheath, and he could not catch his balance. He went over, but this time he pulled his tender nose up, out of the way, and landed on one of his flat lean shoulders.

This hurt, too. Buck lay still several seconds, breathing heavily. Again the will to live surged up strongly. He rolled over on his chest, propped his front legs forward, bringing up his neck and shoulders. Then he brought all his young strength into play and with a mighty twisting lunge, flung his hindquarters upward . . . and caught them there on wide-braced and shaking back legs. He had made it, was really standing on his four small round hoofs, which were still soft, not yet dry. He had passed the first important test of his fitness to live, for now he could suck and have the benefit of the miraculous strength of his mother's first milk.

The mare moved a couple of steps forward, and Buck was thankful for a warm hairy side to lean against. It steadied him. His sense of balance improved rapidly, and along with it came new confidence and new courage. The mare's muzzle was soft and reassuring at his hardly dry hip. He swayed upright and stood alone, without any support. This lasted a long second; then Buck's confidence deserted him, and he rocked back against his mother's side, happily comforted by her warm firm nearness.

At this age nothing was enough to content him very long, however, and only a minute later he pushed away from her and took a step forward—only a half step in truth but bold nonetheless. She met him with a side movement, bringing her flank near his small muzzle. Inner need directed him then. His nose came in contact with something smooth, hot, and tightly swollen. This, something told him, was good, very good, and fine for him. His keen sense of smell pulled him another short step on, and he pushed his long slim head deep under her flank. His upper lip touched something, and stayed with it. This was the waxlike substance that forms on a mare's nipples a day or two prior to the arrival of the foal. Buck put out his tongue and found the secretion sweet and compelling. Pulling his tongue back into his mouth, he savored the new taste to its fullest. It soon began to dissipate down his throat, and eager for more he pushed his muzzle upward and forward again. This time he got more of the wax on his nose, and when he put his tongue out, he found something new there—something warm, sweet, and richly flowing. It entered Buck's mouth, flooded backward and went down his eager young throat, bringing by far the greatest satisfaction and enjoyment of his short life. In less than an hour after his birth, Buck had "stood and sucked," as the Owyhee country ranchers put it, meaning that he was physically strong and able to eat, both of which were important indications of this new foal's good condition.

The vast and rugged Owyhee country is one of the last stronghold of the bands of range horses, generally called wild because of their wariness and fear of men. Naturally timid and cautious creatures, all horses are wild and afraid of people until they have been handled and learn that men are not necessarily enemies. In most instances it is men who provide both the food and care that horses need. But this is not easily learned, especially by horses born in wild freedom.

The country contains the far-flung Owyhee River drainage, including both the numerous and winding forks of the river and its many tributaries. Near its center is the corner where the three states of Oregon, Idaho, and Nevada all touch. It contains high rock-crusted ridges, brushy flat-topped buttes, and foreboding labyrinths of arroyos and twisted canyons. The waters flow in many directions and most, joining in the grassy bottoms, find their way to the great Snake River and eventually, after hundreds of turbulent miles, to the Pacific Ocean.

There are areas of tall trees on the high slopes, but because it is subject to heat and dryness during the summer, much of the land is covered by shrub and dwarfed growths, including juniper, mountain mahogany, and numerous species of cedar. Brush, mostly varieties of sage, is everywhere, and growths of willows and aspen line the water courses, sometimes almost choking them.

The distances in this country are great, and the vistas are usually quiet and lonely. There is peace and leisure and solitude. But this is not always true. Violent storms sometimes come, often in the spring, storms that lash the peaks with lightning flashes, roll echoing thunder along the ridges, and send torrents of water scouring along the bottoms.

Though it was not long after he was born, Buck was up and on his feet, already steady, when the bright round ball of the sun rose and sent its revealing light over this rugged land that first morning. He looked around and saw the rocks and the trees, and the shrubs and low brush. He investigated a nearby limb with his pink nose and found the end unpleasantly sharp and brittle, a fact he would not soon forget. He saw other members of the band, big creatures like his mother, moving slowly about, their heads down in search of browse midst the low brush. One, a big-boned bay off some distance alone, was his father, though that meant nothing to either of them. It was his cream-yellow round-bellied mother that was the center of his big new world. In grazing she moved with short slow steps so he could stay close.

And stay close Buck did. Even while he was looking at all the strange things around him, he cast quick glances to make certain his mother was still there. Soon he turned to her and pushed his muzzle in under her flank, finding a tight full teat at almost the same instant. He sucked vigorously, the short brush of his tail flying about in great delight. When the flow in this teat began to diminish, he switched to the other. Presently no milk was left here either, and Buck pulled back his head and looked around again.

One of the big creatures attracted his attention, and he took a step toward it, but immediately his mother moved between them.

Buck at once forgot the other mare; suddenly he was tired, terribly weary. His legs ached, and his neck, too, from holding up his head so long. His eyelids were so heavy he could hardly keep them open. He knew his slender legs would not support him much longer. He lowered his head. The ground was far away, so far his nose did not touch it. But he had to find some way to get down there. He let his knees bend, and his body started down, and suddenly he was afraid. He did not want to fall again; the ground had been hard, and already his small muzzle was sore. His legs straightened, and head still down, he turned about in a small circle.

Again his knees began to bend, a little at a time, an inch. Then he hesitated. A few seconds later his body relaxed still more; he could not keep awake. Suddenly he was falling; he knew it, and there was nothing he could do about it. Down he went. He managed to hold his muzzle aside, so it would not bang against the gritty soil. His knees hit first; then he flopped to one side, landing on his flat shoulder, down at last on the firm welcoming earth. With a big sigh he let his head down, too, relaxing completely. This was good. And the fall had not hurt nearly as much as he had feared. His mother moved to stand above him. He closed his eyes and a few seconds later was sound asleep.

Though the high Owyhee slopes are usually covered with deep snow in winter, people would sometimes come there during the summer. Some were hikers and nature lovers; others were fishermen or prospectors. Usually they trudged the dusty trails afoot. The horses would see them in the distance, but they seldom got close enough to cause concern. Others who appeared in the swales and on the high ridges were horsemen, big-hatted riders.

On many of the nearby ranches there were cow ponies and riding horses that had come from the range bands, and some were very good ones, surefooted in the rocks and with the speed and agility to head a cow or catch a calf. Most of the ranchers, busy though they were with cattle, kept an eye out for likely-looking three- or four-year-olds without a brand that they might catch and claim for their own. It could prove an easy way to get a good horse, if they were lucky. Also most of them liked the excitement of swinging a long loop over the backs of the wild ones.

Sometimes crews of professional runners came, to catch as many horses as they could for meat-packing plants. They, too, came on horseback, but they were well organized for long grueling runs.

The stallions, jealous of their bands, were always on the

lookout for strange horses, and the mares, especially the old leaders, regarded every mounted horse that came in sight with immediate suspicion.

The spring Buck was born the running began early. He was only three days old. Some might think such a happening would be a calamity for a foal so young, but that is not always true. Even at his tender age, Buck was up and steady on his feet, had already tested his young speed and stamina in leaping frolic around his mother on the slopes. He was so light and quick on his small hoofs that he could almost outrun her when he tried. In fact, he had never seen her go faster than a trot, until that day when the old stallion's angry snorting caused her to lift her head quickly.

The band at the time consisted of seven mares, four yearlings, and three young suckling colts, of which Buck was one. Two of the mares carried foals whose births were not far off.

All the mares were soon alert. Buck's mother turned her head on her long strong neck to look back down the slope. Buck could sense tension in the air. The old stallion snorted again and followed it with a belligerent neigh. The bay lead mare started then, and the others formed a close line behind her.

Buck ran with his mother, bumping at her side. His young eyes rolled about in an effort to see what was the cause of all this. He saw nothing except the gray sage and the rising yellow dust, yet he knew well enough that danger was near.

The dust hung above the slope like a slowly stirring cloud. The horses ahead of Buck and his mother passed into it at a steady trot, and their shapes became dim. The thudding of hard hoofs nearby was strong and regular. Somewhere back in the rear the old stallion's indignant rumbling could be heard, but it held more defiance than fear. Still, the cause of it was beyond Buck's sight or hearing.

Despite the dust, the bay mare who led the band knew what

was back there—a big-hatted rider on a tall strong-legged horse. She was pretty sure, too, that she knew his purpose. This was the way the runs usually started. But she was not badly frightened— not yet. Before them was open country that she knew so well she could follow its trails in the dark. And the band behind her was fresh and strong. She was a lean high-withered mare that had escaped years before from a downcountry ranch, and her leadership was unchallenged.

The continuous running became tedious, and Buck was weary when, near the crest of a short slope, the horses in front slowed to a walk. His mother did, too. A short distance farther on, they halted.

Relieved, Buck sidled to his mother's side and pushed his muzzle in under her flank. Milk was there as he had known it would be. The other suckling foals nursed, too, and the hungry yearlings lowered their heads and searched in the low brush for grass.

Night was coming rapidly, and the lead mare, on the slope above them, was swiveling her long ears to the light breeze and staring into the gathering shadows behind. A big dark bulk came trudging slowly up the rise. It was the stallion, catching up from his place in the rear. He turned across the slope to a position to rest his deformed front foot, then halted and let a deep weary sigh rumble up from his thick throat. Several of the mares, Buck's mother among them, joined the yearlings in the search for grass, and a little later, after a final long look, the lead mare relaxed and lowered her head, too.

Buck sensed that the fear had subsided, and his small stomach was round and pleasantly full, so he folded his long legs and lay down in the first suitably level spot.

The night passed without interruption, and in the morning the sun came up as usual. The mares that had lain down got to their feet slowly and began to search for more grass. Buck followed his mother and insisted on an immediate breakfast, despite the inconvenience her slow steps caused him.

Buck had finished with the first teat and was enthusiastically working on the second when the bay mare above them suddenly wheeled to a high-headed position of attention. At once the others stopped grazing. Buck took his nose from under his mother's flank and looked around, knowing that something was happening.

Down the slope, old Club let out a blast of indignant anger and pawed the graveled earth with his right front foot, the sound one.

Then Buck saw another horse, surprisingly tall, down below on the slope, beyond the stallion. This horse was then standing still, but even while Buck watched, it began to move, coming upward, not fast but steadily. Buck continued to watch, somewhat confused by the stallion's attitude. Then he saw that there was something unusual about the strange horse, a kind of a high hump on its back. Was that the cause of the fear?

Before anything else happened, the bunch started moving, Buck's mother with it. He heard her, turned immediately, and hurried to catch up. Soon they were in the streamer of dust again, traveling mostly at a trot. Sometimes on steep climbs the horses in front slowed to a walk, but the sun was far up before there was a halt.

The lead mare was on a high shoulder, looking back into the valley. The band rested willingly below, the young colts nuzzling hopefully at dusty teats. The stallion was somewhere farther back, and could not be seen, nor could the rider who had been following them. Still, after a long intent look, the bay mare turned and started on. Tired though they were, the others followed without protest.

Later in the afternoon, when they were in a brushy swale, one of the suckling colts, weaker than the others, became played out.

Its slender legs moved slower and slower until presently they stopped entirely. The little creature came to a halt and stood there in the settling dust, too tired to go farther. Its mother, who was also a bay, dark red, old and heavy, halted, too, and swung her round-nosed head for a backward look. She let out a worried little whinny, then turned and made her way back to her exhausted foal.

Aware of this, the lead mare halted, choosing a spot where the view to the rear was good. The others stopped, too.

A short time later old Club came in sight, walking slowly, with his head down, obviously weary. He limped on his bad foot but did not pause. After a time, he noticed the old red mare standing in the brush. Then he, too, stopped and cautiously looked around. Behind him the rider was just coming into sight.

Club swung his head for another backward glance, then started toward the mare. His manner changed, and there was an audible threat in his whinny. The mare lifted her head, saw him, and showed concern. She took a couple of steps toward her foal, which had lain down and was now out of sight in the brush. He did not get up. The mare turned back toward the approaching stallion and waited quietly. She had raised a number of foals in the Owyhee ranges, had been in a dozen or so desperate runs, and old scars on her back and sides were evidence that she knew what this was all about.

Old Club put a new fierceness in his cry as he came on. He flattened his thickened fight-scarred ears, pushed out his heavy muzzle, and bared his great yellow teeth, their broken edges worn to chisel sharpness. Some mares would have given way—especially one of the younger ones more afraid of savage punishment—but not this red bay. Her own weary legs were an argument against more running just then, even if it had not been for the great needs of the thin little creature lying nearby. She waited stolidly.

The stallion hit her with his shoulder, but at a shallow angle or the blow would have knocked her from her front feet. As it was, she had to take two quick steps to stay upright, but then turned immediately back to stand above her foal. With another bellow of rage, Club turned and pounded his way around. He was determined to keep the mare with his band. She calmly turned her rump to him, and his yellow teeth ripped into her dusty hide. His thickly muscled chest hit her, and she moved a few stumbling steps. Again she wheeled back to the colt as soon as she regained her balance.

Jamming his clubbed foot into the ground, the stallion came to a stop a short distance away and regarded the mare with a sullen unhappy stare. Not many would have defied him this long. The horseman behind could be seen, coming out of the swale. Club charged, his jaws spread. Again his teeth brought blood, and again the mare swayed, but she would not flee. She made it plain she would not leave her colt. The stallion snorted his anger and made another charge. This time she avoided his teeth, but the hard blow turned her half around.

"You devil! You mean old devil!" a voice cried angrily.

Both the stallion and the tired mare turned their heads to look.

The rider had put his horse into a gallop and was coming straight at them. He was a young man wearing ranch clothes, his legs long in the stirrups. The long loop of a rope hung from his half-raised right hand. "Git!" he shouted. "Let that mare alone."

The stallion paused, uncertain, half inclined to make a fight of it. He was not afraid of the other horse, not even of the man. But that rope . . . he knew what it was. It caused fear to rise in him, brought back the memory of other times when such a long writhing rope had slid off his back and flanks. Once a loop had settled around his neck, choking him to near unconsciousness before a hard desperate lunge had caused it to break.

The young rider knew horses. Without checking the pace of

his mount, he stood in his stirrups and began swinging the loop about his head, crying again, "Git! Before I lose my temper."

Club could not face that swinging rope. He turned and galloped through the low brush in the direction the band had taken.

The red mare let her head droop wearily and turned her gaze toward the rider, making it plain that he would not be able to drive her from her foal either.

The man reined in his horse and sat, looking at the exhausted mother and her son. "Don't worry, old gal," he told her. "We won't bother you. You're not what we want . . . too old and too young."

While he sat there, letting his horse rest, a second rider appeared from below, halted beside him, and said, "What've you got there?" He nodded his big hat toward the mare.

"Played out, Pop," the younger man answered. "She's got a right young colt lying there in the brush. The stud tried to drive her on, but she wouldn't go. She's got guts. If she wasn't so old, she'd be worth taking, wouldn't she?"

"Maybe," the other man said. "We're looking for riding stock, not chicken feed." Owyhee ranchers did not usually favor mares for saddle use, having found geldings more reliable and even-tempered for ranch work.

"That's right," the son agreed. "But there are some mares in this bunch that would raise some plumb good colts, bred to a good stud like old Rock."

The man smiled. "Raising colts takes time, boy. You're forgetting you're reporting for army duty next week, aren't you?"

"That's only for four years," the younger man answered, "then I'll be back. We'll be needing some good horses. The one I'd like to have is that big yellow mare. She'd make a good mama horse. If we work it right, maybe we can catch her." His eyes sparkled with excitement.

"You'll always be 'needin' ' good horses," the father said. "I guess it's born in you. That mare's got a new colt."

The son nodded. "I saw it. He's a little dandy. We'll take him, too. That's one reason I want her. He ought to make a real classy ropin' horse, with the right kind of training."

"Should," the man agreed. "I kind of like him, too. We've got another day; we'll give it a try."

"Fine." The young man lifted his reins and jerked his head at the red mare. "What'll we do with these?"

"Leave them," his father answered. "They'll get along all right."

When darkness came, the bay mare leading the band halted, lifted her head, and swiveled her long ears around in the direction of their back trail. She pulled in a deep and weary breath as she listened. The other mares stopped and waited, also, the mothers with their young foals at their sides. All of them were tired from the long hours of traveling. The red mare and her foal were missing.

Somewhere back there, too, was the old stallion making his limping progress through the night. Tired also, and sullen because he had been forced to abandon the old mare, Club had slowed his gait to a walk after the last horseman had dropped back and become lost in the gloom. The smell of stirred dust guided him through the darkness, and he knew it would lead him to the band. Presently he saw ahead the dark forms. The mares were busy filling their lank bellies and paid no attention to his arrival. The young foals had already sucked and were lying down. The stallion listened briefly, then lowered his big bony head in search of grass. Movement among the horses lessened and soon ceased entirely.

When the first light of morning came sliding gently over the mountain, the old lead mare was on a nearby rise, searching the awakening land. Those in the band that had lain down got to their feet, and all of them began searching for food. Buck's mother went with them, and he followed close at her side, spreading his long front legs and putting his head down now and then to test the grass the mare ate so eagerly. He found it tough and difficult to manage with his young teeth, and the taste did not appeal to him very much. As food it was, in his opinion, far inferior to milk. As a result of the running, the milk was less abundant than it had been, and whenever his mother stood still long enough, he at once pushed his nose in under her flank.

In a bottom, near a clump of junipers, there was a water hole with clear water, well known to the band. After grazing for a time, the bay mare lifted her head and started toward it. The others followed. Not liking the crowding, the old stallion held back, but the mares went in readily, most of them not stopping until at least their front feet were in the water. They drank thirstily, raised their heads, and then drank some more, still dry from the steady traveling of the previous day. Buck touched his nose to the water, lifted his head, and wrinkled his lips, showing he did not like it. A big red cow lumbered up to the far side, waded in until the water was at her knees, and drank with long gusty pulls. Long-bodied insects rose from the surface and buzzed about, their thin gray wings moving so fast they were hardly visible.

After a time the lead mare pulled her front feet from the mud and moved away, headed up the canyon. The others followed, taking their time. Club moved in for his drink, taking his time, too. There was no rush, and all their feet were sore from yesterday's rocks.

The feed here was thin, and the lead mare kept walking, going, the others knew, to a slope leading up to a wide brushy bench where there was both browse and grass. It was a place that they visited regularly in their constant search for food. The mare had just passed a dark shoulder of bare rock jutting from the canyon wall when suddenly she halted and snapped her head up.

A quick snort came from her nostrils, and an instant later she was off in full flight.

Buck's mother stopped still in her tracks, her head high. Buck knew something was wrong, could feel excitement and danger. Then everything was confused and frightening. All the horses were running, in various directions. Some ran along the bottom, following the lead mare. Others dashed across and tried to climb the opposite wall, and kept slipping and sliding back. Buck's mother followed the lead mare. Buck kept close at her flank. He did not see what was causing the excitement, but he knew it was there. His mother had never before run so wildly.

The lead mare left the canyon and turned up a brushy slope with great digging leaps. Buck's mother followed. Other horses were running behind them. The limbs of the brush were strong and stiff and caused Buck some trouble, but he managed to keep within easy view of his mother. Their hoofs raised dust that drifted on the gentle wind.

The mare up front reached the rim and went out of sight. Buck and his mother continued climbing. When they came to the crest, the yellow mare was puffing from the exertion and slowed her gait to a trot. The lead mare was well into the brush, moving steadily. Other members of the bunch were still on the slope behind, struggling upward through the gray haze of dust.

Buck kept near his mother; he was a little distance to her left, separated by some brush, when she suddenly leaped back into a gallop. Something new had startled her. Buck increased his own speed and stayed even. The lead mare was somewhere in the brush, but Buck could not see her.

A short time later he became aware of an unusually steady drumming of hoofs behind. It did not lessen or go off to one side; instead it increased, gradually getting louder and nearer. Buck sent a quick glance back over his shoulder. A big horse was there, coming with long strong strides, and on its back there was something Buck had never seen before—a man. Buck quickly realized that it was from this horse his mother was fleeing for a reason that was not clear to him—it must be the man on the horse's back.

Buck put on more speed, his slender young legs flying. He was so light and quick that he ran almost without effort, save when he had to change strides or hurdle to avoid the brush. There could be no doubt about his mother's fear.

The yellow mare was running her best, her head straight out. Still the big horse behind, fresher and grain-hardened, continued to gain. Running at one side, Buck saw this. The distance between them lessened until hardly more than a horse's length separated them.

Buck tried to run still faster, to put more room between him and the big horse. He did, forging on ahead of his striving mother. He did not see the loop of the hard-twisted lariat snake out in the air. It flew true, checked an instant above the mare's head, and then dropped about her neck.

Buck did hear the sharp command, "Whoa!" It meant nothing to him of course. Nor did he see his mother, without shortening her stride in the least, suddenly go high in the air and flip over backward. All he knew was that he heard the loud crash of a heavy body in the brush and then his mother was no longer running where he had last seen her. She had disappeared, was gone completely.

Panic gripped the young foal then. More confused and afraid than ever, he lowered his head and really ran, flashing through the brush like a half-white ghost. After the crash, the sounds behind changed, to less pounding, more shouts, and more floundering in the brush.

This increased Buck's fright. He raced on through the sage, came to a deep steep-walled dry wash and, unable to halt, tumbled down into it. The fall knocked the wind from his lungs, and he lay there several seconds without moving. When he did get to his feet, he moved slowly and was somewhat dazed, not knowing whether he was hurt or not. But he did know he was alone, completely alone, for the first time in his young life. That caused a swift return of his desperation. He ran at one of the walls and tried to climb it, but it was too steep and crumbly. His small hoofs sank into the dirt, starting little landslides that, despite all his frantic leaping and plunging, carried him back to the bottom. This happened several times until, struggling in the dust, he lost all sense of direction. He had a great need to run . . . and run. Finally he found a direction in which he could go—along the bottom of the wash.

The bottom was smooth but crooked and winding. Mostly it was dry and dusty, though in places there were shallow little pools and boggy spots. Buck splashed through the water and slipped in the mud. Once he fell and skidded, coating his right side with black slime. Nothing stopped him however. He bounced up and hurried on, around the bends that led first one way and then another. After a time he slowed down and found he was tremendously tired. He went slower and slower; his small slender head drooped lower and lower. Finally, in a patch of sunshine near a steep wall, he halted and became still. Soon the lids slid down over his dark eyes, and he was asleep. It was not long until he awoke, the feeling of fear still deep inside him.

He sent up a small little whinny, a cry of lonesomeness, hoping it would be answered. No answer came. Buck tried once more, then gave up. Something told him that no other horses were nearby, that he would not be answered. He knew he was all alone, and that was the worst thing that could happen, especially to a foal so young and dependent on the help and protections of others. But even in his deep loneliness he did not yet realize how badly he would miss his mother. Without her, in those wild and harsh surroundings, he was almost sure to die.

It was a bad time for the little lost foal, but gradually the fear inside him began to lessen, and the will to live began to make itself felt. He came from tough enduring forebears who had faced dangers and hardship most of their lives, and it was bred in him to try.

The shadow of the steep wall slid across the floor of the wash. Buck shook himself and looked about, alert and wary. He started along the wash, not running but walking, keeping the fears inside under tight control. As time passed, he became bolder and more assured. He would find his mother, and then everything would be all right again.

Presently he came to a place where the wall was low and grass grew on it. Climbing it was easy. He was up on the rim in a few seconds and could look around at a wide expanse of brush-covered slope. It looked like the benchland he last remembered. He could not see any horses; in fact he could not see any movement at all. The gray-green stretches were empty.

There was hope in Buck's look, and an inner sense of direction told him the way to go. He moved through the strong chest-high sage, and kept going. He had to find his mother, and finally, just after sundown, he did.

She lay flat in the brush, coated with fine gray dust. She did not reply to his eager whinny but was still and silent. She made no movement as he approached. He had seen her lying down before, but never stiff and heedless like this. He nudged her, and she paid no attention, did not roll and lunge to get to her feet. Her eyes were open and dull with dust. Her head lay at an unnatural angle to her neck. Buck did not know her neck was broken, but something told him that whatever had given her warmth and movement and caring had gone.

Not knowing what else to do, Buck stood there beside the still yellow form while the sun went down and the deep shadows of night spread across the land.

5

The nearness of the yellow mare and the certainty of her watchfulness and affection had been by far the most important things in Buck's short life, so he curled up close by and stayed with her throughout the cold and cheerless night.

It was a long time until morning. Buck's stomach, accustomed to regular feeding, began to complain about its emptiness. The yellow mare not only had not moved during the night, but her body had become even more rigid and lifeless. Buck did not know what to do.

The sun came up and flooded the long sloping basin with its warmth and light. Nothing within Buck's sight stirred. He got to his feet and switched his small brush of a tail impatiently a couple of times, as if to ask why someone did not come and show him what to do. Though living principally on his mother's milk, he had already begun to follow her example in nibbling at grass. But there were problems. In the first place, he did not much like the taste of the grass; and in the second, his front legs were so long in relation to his neck that he had to spread them wide apart in order to reach the ground. Also his young teeth, hardly protruding through his soft pink gums, were not very efficient in chewing the long thin blades. He much preferred his mother's rich milk.

Buck tried his mother's teats, but nothing came from them. In fact, they were hard, cold, and rigid like the rest of her body. The young foal quickly learned that he would not get any food there and raised his head.

Nowhere nearby could he see any life or movement. The bristly bushes of sage grew on hard gritty reddish soil. What grass there was, was straggly.

A fly settled on Buck's hind leg, well down near the ankle joint. He gave his foot a solid little thump against the ground to dislodge the insect. The fly spun out into the bright morning air, made a big circle, and came back, landing just an inch or so from its former spot. Its bite was sharp when Buck was late in driving it away the second time.

But Buck's most demanding need just then was for something to eat—food. And the only thing he knew that was available was grass. With one front foot back and the other well forward, he managed to get his head down low enough to nibble at some stems. They were dry and not very tasty. He kept at it for some time but found that the stems, after he got them in his mouth, were difficult to chew. It did not seem that he could ever get enough of them to fill his stomach. Becoming discouraged, he raised his head and looked around.

The sun was bright on the gray expanse of sage, but there were still no other horses anywhere. Buck could see nothing that moved, nothing that offered any help. He was terribly lonesome and awfully hungry.

After a time, moving slowly, he returned to the place where his mother lay. She was as he had last seen her, her eyes still dull and her lips drawn back from her big teeth. He went close and stood there for a period of time, but he knew now that it would be useless to try to rouse her. A great change had taken place, and she was no longer the big responsive creature he had known. Buck knew she could not help him, but habit kept him near her until the middle of the afternoon.

His hunger increased. He moved away, searching for something he could eat. He did not find much. The sparse grass was still dry and difficult to chew, and such other growth as he tried was tough and woody. The emptiness in his stomach became more painful, but still the spark inside would not let him give up—not yet. He continued moving, wandering and meandering between the bushes, pausing now and then to try things that looked as if they might be eaten with almost no success.

Night found him in a small ravine. He was weak from hunger and made no effort to return to the place where his mother lay. It was not only too far for his weary legs, but it would be useless; she could not help him. He found a bit of smooth clear earth and lay down on it, pulling his hind legs up in a curl like a big dog. Tired and low in resistance, he slept but awoke several times to listen in the darkness.

He was awake when the first light came, which is regularly the time when animals stir and start to seek food. But Buck continued to lie there, finding it easier than to get to his tired legs and begin again the discouraging search of the previous afternoon. The sun came up, and its rays warmed him to new hope. He got to his feet and stood there for a while, just looking around. The brush was bright under the sun but without movement, except for a gentle stirring in the morning breeze.

Buck spread his front legs and nosed a bit of low vegetation, having learned by now that this was usually the tenderest. The plant, however, turned out to be a disagreeable weed. He left it and began wandering through the brush. His steps were slow, and he made frequent halts, nibbling and testing.

Some time later, at a time when his head was up, he saw something that attracted his immediate interest—a movement in the brush. He watched alertly, and it proved to be another animal, though not a horse. It was almost as big as he was, and it had a thick round body with long slender legs. Its color was tawny yellow, with dark bars across the underside of its neck, which was a creamy white. It had big dark eyes and short black horns, curiously divided into two prongs near the tips.

Something told Buck that this new creature, while not a horse, was not dangerous to him, either. He moved toward it, uttering an eager little whinny.

The antelope raised its trim head and watched the young foal advance. During its life in the high sage flats, it had seen many horses, and knew it had nothing to fear from them. In fact, it is not uncommon for horses and antelope to graze close together, each welcoming the others' alertness in spotting any approaching danger and giving a warning alarm.

Nearing the antelope Buck paused, not entirely sure of himself. He felt the animal would not harm him, and its nearness was a great relief to his loneliness, but it offered no visible welcome. It had not replied to his whinny.

Buck pushed out his nose. The antelope responded by slowly extending its own shining black muzzle. The welcoming touch was brief, however, only for the space of a few deep smells, before the antelope, which was a mature buck, lost interest and looked away. Buck went closer and extended his nose to the new creature's hairy flank, as he had done when telling his mother he was hungry. At that the antelope swung its head about in irritation, and a point of one of its black horns struck Buck's neck, causing a disagreeable pain. In some surprise Buck backed off quickly.

The antelope lowered its head and with its strong white teeth began to nibble at the bushes. It ate with an evident satisfaction that at once interested Buck. He noted that it took mostly twig tips. Obviously the antelope liked them. After watching a few seconds, Buck decided he would try. He reached out, wrapped his lips about a convenient small limb, and bit off its end. That was easy to do, but the chewing was more difficult. He kept at it.

until the mass went down his throat. It did not taste very good, but the feeling inside his stomach was pleasant, certainly better than the emptiness. He moved to another twig.

While far from being as quick and efficient as the antelope, Buck was steadily searching for browse when, not much later, the antelope lifted its head for a sweeping look around with its remarkably keen vision. In one direction his eyes stopped, and his big scooplike ears wheeled forward in a way that caused Buck to follow the gaze.

A small brownish-gray creature was sliding silently through the shadows of the brush. It was thick-bodied and had a long bushy gray tail that extended straight out behind. It was a prairie wolf, more commonly known as a coyote. Just then it paused and, one front paw lifted, stood looking at Buck and the antelope.

The coyote was small in size in comparison with Buck and did not seem dangerous; the antelope, however, continued to watch it closely. They stayed like this, neither moving, for several seconds. A short time later, another wolf—this one the same in color but somewhat larger than the first—made its appearance. It came from a different direction, but the antelope knew of its presence immediately and swung its dark nose around. Buck looked, too. Half concealed by a clump of sage, the second wolf had its yellow eyes fastened on them intently.

The antelope stamped a split forehoof impatiently, and his short white-tufted tail rose above his back. Buck tried to watch the coyote, which was now in motion, but most of the time it was nothing more than a gray shadow flitting through brush. Still Buck was not particularly afraid, having seen the small wolves once before, when he was with his mother. They had not come close.

A stamping sound brought the colt's attention back to the antelope. It was hitting the earth nervously with its feet, and the short white tail was more stiffly erect than before. There was a ridge of bristling hair along the antelope's back, and in the sunlight, its rump patch was brightly white.

Any wild animal would quickly recognize this as a danger signal. Buck wheeled about to see in which direction the danger might be. He did not connect it immediately with the fleeting gray shadows, and saw nothing else that might be the cause of it. Then he heard a swift drumming of hoofs.

Buck turned back and saw that the antelope was leaving, bounding away at high speed, its rump patch winking whitely. Such sudden flight was highly alarming. Buck leaped into a run, too, following the antelope, which was the closest thing he had to a friend. He ran as fast as he could, trying to catch up, but he was already weary, and the brush was thick and troublesome. The antelope would not wait. It paid no attention to Buck's entreating whinnies, and its white rump became steadily smaller in the distance. After a time it went into a fold in the earth's surface and was lost completely.

Buck kept running but soon slowed, realizing the hopelessness of it. The antelope had not been very friendly anyway. What Buck wanted more than anything else was another horse—a bunch of them would be best, but even just one would do. He came to a halt and carefully looked all around. The expanse of brush was discouraging. Buck could see nothing moving, not the white flash of an antelope nor anything else. There was nothing to indicate to him that there was any other living thing in his world. But there was. In a small opening not far away, a stealthy gray movement came to a halt.

The weariness in Buck's legs suddenly became so intense they could no longer hold him erect. The big knobby joints failed, and he went down with a thump, landing sprawled out in the low brush. He was still for a moment, then lowered his head to the dust and relaxed completely, so weak and hungry that he no longer cared. Nothing seemed important anymore, except just to lie there. The sun was hot on his small body, and he had not had anything to drink for hours, but now even that did not seem very important.

The coyote stood on three slender and tireless legs, the left front one half-lifted as it watched the small yellow shape. Presently it raised the entire front of its body until it could see over the brush and looked all around. Over and beyond the place where the colt lay, it caught a glimpse of another gray form and knew the other coyote was ranging through the bushes there. Lowering its front paws back to the ground, the first wolf opened its mouth and let its red tongue loll out, panting softly from the recent running.

The other coyote worked in closer, on soft silent paws. Coming to a full view of the little opening in which Buck slept, it halted. Horses were much larger creatures than coyotes usually sought for food, and they had hard powerful hoofs. But this one was very small, and not very wise, and all alone. Horsemeat was also good food, even that on dried withered carcasses found in deep ravines.

The coyote took a few more soft steps forward, and then beyond Buck, it could see its mate stealthily working his way forward, too. The little foal would supply not only food for them; there would also be plenty for the four hungry pups waiting in the den under a big half-buried boulder not far away.

The larger coyote licked its lips and crept forward, then paused to half rise for a final look around. Once before, when he had tried to slip up on a sleeping foal like this, there had been a sudden rush of big horses, and they had slammed their hard hoofs into his ribs, and he did not want that to happen again.

On the other side the mother, bolder and hungrier, pushed her way forward, belly to the gritty red soil. She advanced a few feet, then lay still, her unblinking yellow eyes fixed on Buck's motionless shape. Once caution broke through Buck's great weariness, and he raised his head for a look around. Quickly both wolves froze to tense gray statues and remained that way until the foal let his head sink back to the ground. Seconds later they resumed their slow careful approach, coming from different directions. Only a little closer and they could dash forward and have their long yellow fangs deep in Buck's flesh before he was fully awake. Being experienced predators, they knew well the vulnerable places to attack, such as the throat and the tendons of the hind legs. Once Buck was crippled and bleeding, it would be only a matter of time until they could finish him off. Then, after eating until they were full, they would chew off chunks of the meat to take to the pups.

But then, just seconds before they would spring, the silence was interrupted by a new sound, one that caused both wolves to freeze instinctively.

After the two riders had left her, to follow the club-footed stallion, the old red mare had moved through the low brush to a position above her young foal, which was also red, and put down her nose to nuzzle it. The little creature lifted his head in slow response and then lowered it again, too weak to do more.

They stayed there all the rest of that long hot afternoon, scarcely moving in their weariness. Finally the sun went down and the air became cooler. The mare bent to nuzzle the foal, fully awake, then started off through the brush. After a dozen or so steps she halted and sent back a soft cry of entreaty. The colt did not answer immediately, but the mare waited patiently. Finally the long legs stirred, and on the second try, the foal managed to get to his feet. He swayed dangerously, steadied himself, and made his way to the mare. She did not move while he nursed, at first halfheartedly but later with more vigor. When he presently left off and looked around, his eyes were brighter.

The mare again moved through the sage. The foal did not follow her, and again she halted and waited. Full night had come now, and the heat was gone from the slope. The foal came up to her, moving slowly.

On through the darkness she measured her pace to his, going with slow steps, halting whenever he did, encouraging him with her soft whinnies. And somehow he stayed on his weary legs and kept coming.

Near midnight a dark bulk appeared in front of them, which the mare knew to be trees. She made her way to them without hesitation and, not waiting for the foal, went on to the star shine of a pool, lowered her head and drank, shallowly at first and afterward deeply. Then she turned, went back to the foal, and nuzzled him with her wet cool muzzle. He perked up and followed her back to the water.

They stayed there the rest of that night. Both lay down, and both got up repeatedly in the darkness to go into the water where the mare drank deeply. When morning came, the mare got up, took another long drink, and left the trees to graze. The foal came a short time later, and she let him nurse until all the milk was gone.

The country about them was the familiar brushy slopes backed by rock-crusted ridges, with green pools and runs of juniper and cedar and mountain mahogany. A small band of mule deer, does and young fawns, came, pausing to browse off the new leaves on the lower limbs of the mountain mahogany, and made its way to the water hole in the junipers to drink.

Having sucked, the red foal found a smooth spot and lay down, relaxing his thin body thankfully. The mare, though fully aware of him, continued grazing industriously, at regular intervals lifting her bony head to look around. By feeding in circles, she stayed close to the place where the foal was bedded, and once she approached and let him nurse again. He nibbled some grass briefly before again lying down.

The sun was near its midmorning height when the mare lifted her head and went to the water hole. The mule deer—mothers and young alike—were curled in old depressions in the juniper shade and paid no attention to the horse. She went to the water

35

and drank in easy unhurried sips. Finishing, she returned to the open, neighed softly to her foal, and moved off through the brush.

The colt got to his feet at once, as if the message had been completely understood, and followed her. He moved forward steadily, and it was apparent that his condition had greatly improved during the night and morning. The mare walked slowly, pausing now and then to nibble at convenient browse, and the foal had no difficulty in keeping at her heels.

Her desire was to rejoin the band, and the path she followed was scarred by new hoof marks. It was not these that guided her, however, but the smell of dust, which hung in the air though it could no longer be seen. In places this smell was faint and in others strong, depending on the ground's condition. She followed it until the midday heat forced her to stop near a pothole in the shade of a rock face.

In midafternoon she roused the colt, and they went on, coming in a short time to the crest of a brushy hogback, which in addition to the dust had a strong smell of manure. It was where the band had spent the first night after she had been left in the brush.

Taking some food as she walked, the mare continued until late afternoon before searching out an area of better grass and lowering her head for serious grazing. The colt nursed, then followed a while nibbling before lying down. They passed the night beside the clear riffle of a small creek, and by morning both of them were visibly rested and stronger. The mare grazed for an hour, then searched out the dust smell and started traveling.

It was in the afternoon that, after climbing a gentle rise, the red mare came to a small crest and saw a short distance away in the brush what she had been so determinedly looking for—another horse. But it was not much of a horse, just a small washed-out yellow colt as pitifully thin as her own foal at her heels. This colt was alert, on its feet, and having heard her coming, was looking in her direction as she topped the rise. Raising his head, he sent out a long and joyous whinny. The mare halted, a bit confused at one so small all alone.

There was, however, no doubt in Buck. At once he set out through the brush for her at a gallop, his gait a bit wavering but still a gallop. A gray prairie wolf leaped aside from his path, stopping in midflight after a couple of strides. Buck did not seem to notice it. The mare, however, did. After a quick glance back at her foal, she lowered her blunted head and started in the wolf's direction at a menacing trot. The animal immediately resumed its flight, and a second later disappeared in the brush. Beyond him there was the swift motion of his mate.

Having accomplished her purpose, the red mare halted. Buck came on in his rush, uttering another happy neigh. The mare turned her head for a glance around, knowing it was not right for a foal this young to be alone. Still there was no sign of any other horses.

Buck arrived. He probably knew this was not his mother, but even so he was so happy and so hungry that it made little difference. He rushed in headlong and pushed his small muzzle under the red flank, and had one of the dark nipples between his lips before the mare hardly knew what had happened. That was not her intention; she had her own young to feed. Bending her neck, she nipped Buck smartly on his yellow flank. He paid no attention but continued gulping the milk down his throat as rapidly as he could swallow. She lifted a hind leg and knocked him loose. He knew what she meant and stood and looked at her, the milk he had already gotten churning pleasantly in his stomach.

Buck was so relieved at having the companionship of his own kind that the rebuff was really not important to him. The main thing was that he was no longer alone. A minute later he went over and touched noses with the red colt, which was only a few days older than he was and about the same size.

After making certain no other horses were around, the mare grazed for a time. Then she lifted her head and ambled on through the brush, still following the dust scent. Buck followed, with another eager whinny, not having the slightest intention of being left behind. During the past two days he had had enough loneliness to last him the rest of his life. He even forced his way into a position between the mare's heels and the red colt, but learned better of this when the mare turned with her ears threateningly flattened.

When next the mare halted and indicated that she was ready to be nursed, Buck timed himself and moved in with the red colt. He grabbed a full nipple and got several big gulps before the mare's teeth hit him. He paid no attention to the bite, and the mare brought a leg forward and knocked both colts loose. The red one went back immediately, but Buck waited warily until the mother's vigilance lessened, then slipped in for a few final pulls before the mare got rid of them both by walking on. Buck and the red colt trailed after her.

In the days that followed, this happened again and again. Knowing well what real hunger was, Buck kept alert and quick. Whenever the mare indicated she was ready to be sucked, he hurried into position. She continued to rebuff him with teeth and legs, but this was frequently complicated by the presence of her own colt. The punishment was not really serious and did not keep Buck from returning at every opportunity. His rump soon showed a lot of teeth marks, but he got more and more milk. Although she was not his own mother, the red mare was a wonderful substitute, and he followed her just as determinedly as he had the yellow mare.

More days passed, and Buck's sunken flanks began to fill out. In addition to the new milk, he worked hard at whatever grass and browse he could find. The mare continued her slow traveling, seeking out grassy swales and watering places. Generally she was close enough behind other horses to follow their scent in the dust but too slow to catch them. Her calmness and patience soon eased the fear and confusion that had begun to grow inside Buck. Life was good, even though there were only the three of them. Buck and the red colt came to know each other well and got along. In the cool evenings they played together, and the mare accepted Buck more and more.

Then one bright summer afternoon they topped a rock-crusted ridge on a worn winding trail and found the meadow on the other side dotted with horses of various colors. The mare stopped and let out a pleased neigh; this was what she had been intending. Now she and the foals would be in a complete band, with a leader and a stallion. She started downward, and the two young colts followed. By this time Buck felt as much a part of the family as if he had been born into it, and the red mare did not seem to feel any difference.

A challenge came up from the meadow, and a thick-necked horse down there stood with its head high. The red mare did not reply, nor did she pause. It was a stallion's usual challenge. Moreover, it was old Club's voice, which meant it was her own old bunch. That only a few weeks before the stallion had savagely attacked her in the attempt to make her leave her foal was now of no importance. She went down and entered the band. Old Club's show of distrust vanished, and he ignored her, returning to his grazing. The mares merely lifted their heads for a brief look at the three horses, and before many minutes had passed, it was almost as if they had never been away.

Back in the security and company of the bunch, and now fully accepted by his new mother, Buck throve. He grew in height and filled out in flanks and rump. Bigger and stronger than his foster brother, he was quicker and more aggressive at nursing

time and got the bigger share of the milk. As is usual among animals, the red colt did not seem to hold this against Buck; whether following the mare or playing, they were almost constantly together.

The weather was hot, but there were cool breezes along the slopes in the late afternoon. The wise horses sought out the better grass in the protected ravines and on the creek banks. Some adopted the habit of the deer and ate the new growth on the lower branches of mountain mahogany. The flanks and ribs of the mares filled out, and the suckling foals grew rapidly, becoming both taller and stronger. Buck's creamy-yellow coat took on a bright shine, and he was one of the hardiest and quickest in the bunch, going up over the rocks like a mountain goat whenever he wished. At the creeks and springs he liked to play in the water, wading in and splashing it with his front feet.

They saw people occasionally watching them from a distance. A lot of them were hikers, on foot, and these were easy to evade. Others were on horseback, which made them different. The wise old lead mares kept track of them from the high points, and almost anything that looked like an attempt to get near was reason enough for an alert.

Some of the horsemen were from the low-lying ranches, and their principal interest was merely to spook the wild bands back, to keep them away from their fences and tame mares. Range stallions down among the pastures and fields could do a lot of damage, much of it to themselves from the barbed wire. That was the way old Club had gotten his deformed foot, as the white scar line just above the hoof showed.

Other horsemen, however, had a different idea. They could not resist giving the wild ones a run, hoping to get their ropes on a good young one or maybe drive the whole band into a trap where they could take their time and pick out whichever ones they wanted. Sometimes they would take the whole bunch and sell the unwanted ones to the packinghouses.

The lead mare and the stallion had no way of telling the men's intentions when they appeared, and as a result, all riders were viewed with immediate suspicion. Anything that looked like an attempt to approach or surround the band was enough to start it moving.

Late that summer two men on horseback appeared and chased the bunch one afternoon for a couple of hours along a long ridge. They never really got close. The wily old lead mare set the pace at a sharp trot, and Club brought up the rear, pausing every now and then to look back and send out deep grumblings from his throat. The men, of course, would be carrying ropes.

Buck felt the excitement, and his trot was high and light as he moved beside the red colt at the heels of the old mare. He knew something was happening, but it did not worry him very much because the countryside was vast and he felt that he could run and run and that nothing could catch him.

The riders broke off the pursuit while the sun was still well up and were soon left out of sight. The lead mare was alert and watchful the rest of the afternoon and all the next day, keeping to the high rims. The men did not reappear, and soon things in the band settled back to normal. There was time for sleeping and grazing, and for gathering on the ridges in the later afternoons where the stiff breezes discouraged the insect pests.

It was good that they had this time, putting layers of solid flesh on their ribs, because a morning came when the ground was covered by a white mantle of snow. Buck had never seen snow before and, after the first surprise at its softness, paid little attention to it. The lead mare knew, however, the time had come to start for the band's regular winter range in the lower river breaks. Buck and his foster brother followed the red mare across the windswept slopes.

They had reached the bottoms of the steep-walled canyons when the first hard blizzard drove its burden of frozen snow along the high dark rims. The weeks and months that came afterward were cold and bitter, but there were only a few days of hard crust on the snow when frost-cured grass could not be dug from the pockets near the creeks. Some scrub browse was found, too.

Still there were losses, such as occurred almost every winter. An old brown mare left the bunch one afternoon, trudged over a low splinter ridge, and did not return. Also, early one morning as Buck and his little foster brother followed the red mare along a narrow creek bank, a great tawny cat leaped suddenly from a nearby hiding place. Buck fled in panic, but the red colt was caught. He had never been as quick and strong as Buck and had not developed as well. The cougar landed on the red colt's shoulders in a great long leap that knocked the little creature flat. The old mare wheeled and whinnied and blustered, but before she could get up enough courage to move in, the unequal struggle was over.

Buck was jittery and cautious for days afterward and missed the companionship of the other colt. It was really to his benefit, however, since he no longer had to share the mother's milk. Born on the range herself, the old mare's lot had often been one of tragedy and hardship, and she got over the loss in a few days.

Otherwise the winter was uneventful, and in the spring they made their way to the south slopes, where new grass always first appeared. This grass had little strength, and they moved slowly. The grass became thicker and had more body, and their flanks began to fill out, and their ribs started to sink back into their bodies. They sought big rocks and tall brush to rub against, and the dry dead hair came loose in dusty little clouds.

Buck followed his adopted mother these days as though she were his own. Indeed, it was doubtful if either of them remembered she was not. But now, carrying another foal in her big belly, she desired to wean him and would nip him vigorously and painfully when he tried to suck. Not many such experiences were necessary before Buck got the idea, and his attempts to nurse became fewer and fewer until finally he gave up entirely. For a time he missed the daily milk, but soon learned that he could make up for the loss by spending more time in search of the spring grass and browse. It was a good time of the year for the horses, and Buck continued to grow and develop. Inside him there were hidden wells of energy that, as the weather became warmer and the days longer, made him want to run and gallop and kick up his heels, which he did. Other yearlings in the band felt the same way, and they played games of follow the leader. On bright mornings they raced about in circles, chasing each other in the grassy meadows, and reared and pawed and nipped playfully, unaware that this was training for the time when these things would be done more seriously.

Buck was among the strongest of them and found that he could run as swiftly as any. Also he could dance as long on his hind feet and feint as deftly with his round front hoofs.

These were good days, days when there was plenty to eat and plenty of time for noon-day napping in the pleasant shade of the juniper groves. The water in the creeks was cool and filling. Red cattle with white on their necks and heads began to appear on the lower slopes. Occasional horsemen were seen, and several weeks later two of them gave the bunch a run, but it only lasted a day. Buck was never afraid and, in truth, rather enjoyed the excitement.

At night he still sought out his foster mother, from long habit, to sleep near her. One morning he was surprised and almost frightened to find a stranger in their group, a gangling little filly that seemed mostly neck, legs, and ears. She had been born during the night. Highly curious when he got over his surprise, Buck moved closer to sniff the little creature. Then he got a second surprise and shock. The old red mare flattened back her ears and bared her teeth. He had seen her do this before, but it had always been at others, never at him. He could hardly believe it until a couple of threatening steps in his direction told him she really meant it. The filly was hers, and there would be no foolishness about it.

Buck moved away promptly. The mare's ears relaxed, but she had made her point so clearly that when a short time later the filly, curious herself, tried to approach Buck, he warily retreated. This new little creature was obviously something special and precious in the red mare's eyes.

An adjustment was necessary, and it did not take Buck long to make it. He could, he learned, still stay with the group and be with the red mare, but the place at her side, whether resting, feeding, or traveling, was strictly reserved for the filly. So long as Buck remembered this, he found he had no trouble. Consequently the three of them were together much of the time. Such a three-member family group can frequently be seen in range-horse bands where man does not interfere in their lives.

Life in the bunch soon became much as it had been. Buck found that he had more freedom, more time in which to choose his activities, what he should do and when. This did not prove difficult. Other yearlings were in the same situation, with mothers that had new colts. They, too, had time to play and welcomed the running and galloping.

For Buck, life was cheerful and good, with plenty of feed and plenty of exhilarating companionship. He became the leader in the play and games, teasing the others. Then one bright morning his contentment was shattered. He was run out of the band.

Buck had finished his early morning grazing and was restless. It was a fine summer day; the sun already high in the sky was shining warmly. He moved on light hoofs through the meadow in search of something to do. He came to another yearling, a trim filly he knew well. After greeting her with a friendly sniff, he began teasing her for a romp of running and leaping. The afternoon before, he remembered, three of them, all yearlings, had had a great time, racing about over the grass and kicking their heels up at the sky. They had engaged in numerous fake battles, rearing and pawing with their front feet, then whirling to threaten each other with half-kicking motions of their rumps and rear hoofs.

The filly did not immediately accept Buck's invitation, and he pushed against her with his shoulder, causing her to take a couple of off-balance steps. Then he stretched his strong neck over and nipped her just in front of the withers as he had done several times before. She let out a little squeal of protest and wheeled her rump around to threaten him with her heels, but he knew she did not really mean it and nipped her again. Big and bold for her age, she took off with a bound. Delighted, Buck followed, digging his hard hoofs into the springy meadow turf. He was certain he could catch her, and soon did.

Running in a circle, the filly dodged among the grazing mares and their suckling foals. Several lifted their heads and put back their ears. Another yearling, a little black mare, galloped to get in front of the filly and join the fun. She ducked back, ran past Buck, and he raced after her. She made a quick spin in another direction. Not expecting this, Buck had to make a wider turn and lost ground. She halted and stood watching him, her eyes bright with glee and challenge. Buck pranced toward her, feeling very big and important. That was when he was hit.

Buck never saw the other horse coming. The first he knew of the attack was when a solid blow sent him reeling over into the short grass. He almost lost his footing but managed to keep it and gave a quick glance over his shoulder. What he saw was a shocking surprise. Another horse, looking huge, was bearing down on him with teeth bared and ears clamped back tight against the poll of its neck.

Buck wheeled aside, but even so took a half blow on his flank that numbed him. He watched the other horse turn back with a limping foot and knew it was old Club. This shocked him still more because until now the stallion had never paid any attention to him, had never even seemed to see him.

But there could be no doubt that the stallion saw him now, nor was there any question about what he intended to do. Club's small eyes were filled with anger and rage, and the wide yellow teeth that lined his opened mouth were ready to snap. Fear leaped inside Buck, and he turned and fled, though not quickly enough to avoid a slash across his rump. The pain stabbed at him, adding to the fear. He put down his head and ran with all the speed in his strong legs—really ran.

The pursuit, heavy and uneven, sounded close behind. Buck kept on running. He went across the grass and was in the brush before he realized that the sound behind him had ceased. Slowing his gait, he took a cautious look back and saw that Old Club had stopped. He stood at the edge of the meadow and his posture and manner showed clearly that he had not relented. On the contrary, his lowered thrust-forward head was a plain warning to Buck not to return.

Returning was the last thing in Buck's mind just then. The gash on his rump still burned painfully, and he did not want to risk another one. He was also awed and shaken by the raw fierceness of the old horse's rage.

Buck did the only thing he could do. That was to wait, hoping Club would forgive him, or forget, whatever it was he had done. Time passed, and Club remained plainly on guard, giving no indication that he would do either. Buck waited and waited, but the old stallion knew that game, too. It was only when the band moved into a juniper thicket for the midday napping that Club left his position and trudged up to the trees.

After a time Buck cautiously followed. As he approached the grove, he saw the old stallion's dark form in the near shadow, and that was all that was needed to stop him.

Halting, Buck found himself alone, for the first time since that long-ago memory of his mother's death. He missed the other horses keenly, their companionship and nearness, their breathing and sighing, the slow plod of their hoofs as they moved in the grass. The sage, though he had lived in it most of his life, seemed big and strange. Panic began to rise inside him, as it had at the time he lost his mother. He felt abandoned and unprotected, and wanted to run and hide where he could not be seen.

But most of all he wanted to be back with the others. The band was his home. All his knowledge and habits revolved around it. He wanted to be with his foster mother. That the little filly would be between them was unimportant. All he needed was to see the mare, to hear her, and know she was there. Lifting his muzzle, he sent out a long pleading whinny, hoping his foster mother would appear or at least answer. But the mare did neither; nothing happened. The old stallion did not even change his position on guard.

Buck's head drooped, and he was sad. He had been abandoned; none of them cared anything about him. He did not know what to do. He did not want to do anything that would arouse the old stallion's temper again; he was certain about that. Those slashing teeth left marks that burned and hurt a long time. He did not even think of resisting, knowing he could not outface Club's ferocity.

Still Buck did not turn and go off into the brush or over a ridge to some place where he could not be seen. Old Club's presence, as glowering as it was, was better than being completely alone. And the other horses, though still among the junipers, would come out to graze when it became cooler.

The band did appear later, and Buck neighed with happy anticipation when he saw them. But they paid no attention to him and scattered at once to feed. Old Club put his head down, too, but grazed where he could keep a watchful eye on the yellow yearling.

Buck neighed again with no better results. Still he could not take his attention from the other horses, not even to eat. Night came, and he could not see them, but that did not make it any better. He missed them even more, and the dark stillness all around increased his fear and loneliness. In time this fear became more powerful than the threat of the old stallion. He began to make his way slowly and quietly through the brush, toward the place where he knew the band would be bedded on a shallow slope.

They were dark shapes in the gloom, and several lifted their heads as Buck moved in among them. He searched silently until he found his foster mother. She was on her feet, which is the way older horses frequently sleep, and awoke as he approached. The filly, who was curled at her mother's feet, pushed her little nose toward Buck without getting up.

Buck sniffed the filly and then touched noses with the mare, delighted to be back with them. Both horses immediately went back to sleep, and Buck found a place nearby and lay down, feeling that everything was all right again.

The rest of the night was quiet. Buck neither saw nor heard anything of the old stallion, and he was thankful for that. He wanted no more notice from Club.

When light came, the band got to its feet and moved out to graze. Buck trailed after the red mare and her filly. He was hungry and applied himself busily to the grass, which was withered and dry but filling. The horses were scattered across the upper end of a small basin.

Shortly after midmorning the old lead mare lifted her head and started up a slope. The others followed dutifully, but in a straggling unhurried manner. On this pleasant sunny morning there was plenty of time. Buck ambled behind the red mare and her filly.

Over the ridge the lead mare found grass that suited her and lowered her head. The others scattered into the brush, eating as they went. The red mare ate steadily, but the filly was not much interested in grass. She moved toward Buck and extended her nose. The mare was not so protective now and paid no attention to them. After a sniff Buck returned to his browsing.

Later the band went to a small creek that gurgled softly down through a meadow. They drank, taking their time, and then made their way to a thick shady grove of young willows where the flies would be less annoying. Most of the younger animals lay down. The red mare and several of the others rolled, coating themselves with fine gray dust, which provided extra protection against insect pests.

They stayed there during the heat of the day, lazily switching their tails. The shadow of the high ridge was falling half across the swale when the lead mare took them back to the grass. The grass was good and strong, and Buck moved into it happily. The red mare grazed not far away, and the filly leaped and frolicked around her in close little circles.

Buck ate until he was comfortably full, and then left his foster mother and the filly to walk through the meadow. Soon he saw a yearling who was one of his playmates and went to greet her with a touch of noses. She turned away in a gallop, and Buck dashed after her, knowing this was an invitation for a romp. She ran in a small circle, going among the mares, which caused some with young foals to put back their ears in irritation. But she was having too much fun to pay any heed to them. And so was Buck.

Their circles widened, and suddenly as they were passing, one of the older horses leaped at Buck, striking him on the shoulder. Buck almost fell, but managed to right himself and looked to see who had made the attack. Then he remembered. It was old Club again, coming at him with flattened ears and teeth spread.

Buck bolted away, knowing it to be the only thing to do. The old stallion was in a rage. Despite Buck's quickness, those great ragged teeth cut into his rump, not far from the bite he had received the previous day. It hurt. Buck thought of nothing but the need to escape. Thrusting out his head, he ran with all the strength in his strong young legs. For a few strides there was the sound of heavy pounding behind him. This soon lessened and stopped.

When he was sure that the pursuit had halted, Buck turned and looked back, and saw that the situation was the same as it had been the afternoon before. Club was standing guard, and beyond him the mares and colts were going about their various activities of nursing or grazing as calmly as if nothing out of the ordinary had happened. Buck let out a long plaintive neigh. No

one paid any attention to it, not even his foster mother, the old red mare.

And nothing out of the ordinary had happened. It was entirely normal for the old stallion in a band to run young studs out of the bunch—even their own sons, as in Buck's case—whenever they got old enough to become rivals for the attention of the mares. It was nature's own method of selective breeding. The red mare had been present numerous times before when this had happened.

Untamed as they were for centuries, the range horses were bred, born, and lived all their lives in wild groups, bands, and bunches of varying sizes. They ate together, traveled together, and rested together, coming to depend on this close communal existence for such all-important things as safety and protection. They developed habits and routines that became ingrained in their very natures. When one was afraid, it alerted the others. One running would start the others. A leader was necessary; otherwise they were likely to mill around in confusion. When one went to drink, they all went. So out there alone in the sage, Buck's deep uneasiness and desire for the companionship of other horses were only natural. Flight was his principal method of defense. He had been born ready to run, had got up on his four able young legs almost at once. Speed he had, but he needed a warning system, too. That was where the band became very important; a dozen pairs of eyes saw more than one pair. Twenty-four ears, especially when widely scattered in a meadow, heard more than two.

Buck, of course, did not have the power to reason this out. All he knew was that he was nervous and without guidance. There was no one for him to follow, and, like many young horses, he lacked the courage and the experience to strike out on his own.

He was much concerned about his situation, but there seemed

to be no solution to it. Plainly old Club had no intention of permitting him to live any longer with the bunch. All Buck could do was to hang around the fringes and keep the other horses in sight. This helped, not much but some, and in the succeeding days Buck had to accept it. The needs of food, water, rest, and sleep were unavoidable, and they took much of his time, but on the ridge or in the valley, whether within sight or not, he always kept track of the band and knew where it was. At night he usually slept within sound of the others, most of the time on his feet now, the position in which he felt best prepared to defend himself. He made several more attempts to slip back into the band, but each time old Club soon discovered him and chased him away. This got to be routine, and Buck headed into the brush as soon as Club started in his direction. That was the situation a couple of weeks later when something else unexpected happened.

A strange horse appeared in the upper end of a small basin in which Club's band was feeding. The old lead mare saw it at once. Club followed her gaze and after a few seconds let out a questioning neigh. The newcomer halted but did not reply. A moment or so later it lowered its head and began to graze. Club relaxed then, knowing the stranger to be a mare. She was as far as he was concerned welcome to join the bunch, which she might be expected to do, though it was plain from her behavior that she was not in any hurry.

From his usual place apart from the others, Buck watched the newcomer with keen interest. Her presence had a suggestion of company, and company was something he needed. He did not hurry to approach the stranger, however, because of a natural timidity toward things and creatures new and unknown.

The new mare was not alone. Other horses soon appeared from the trees behind her. These, too, grazed as they moved and gave little attention to Club's band, though each new arrival increased Buck's excitement. He saw that there were half a dozen or so of them altogether, including two that he knew by their size to be young foals. They fed steadily toward Club's bunch, and his mares, in turn, began working their way upward. The mares continued grazing, but Club, though he stayed close to them, did not lower his head.

There was one horse in the other group—a paint—that was acting edgy, too, and Buck from his position where he could see both bands sensed that something unusual was going on. He watched eagerly.

The paint horse was black with wide splashes of white on his heavy body. He had an irregular streak of white down his face, too. A patch of white ran across his thick withers, taking in about a third of his thick tangled mane.

In contrast old Club was a bright red bay in color, with black mane and tail and black lower legs, though both hind feet were white, this color extending upward a short distance.

Slowly but surely the two wild bands decreased the distance between them. Coming close, two of the mares sniffed each other. One switched her tail with a show of irritation, but nothing came of it. Both lowered their heads and continued grazing. This happened several times as the bands mingled. Nothing else happened, but Buck could feel the tension. He knew by now that the paint was also a stallion. Both he and Club walked stiffly, Club no longer showing any sign of his limp.

Except for the way they moved, neither gave any outward sign that he was aware of the other's presence as the gradual mixing of the mares brought them closer and closer together. At last the invisible barrier was crossed. Club wheeled and charged, his ears plastered back tight against his neck, his mouth open, his teeth bared.

The paint horse had known what all this was building up to and was ready. He set himself, balancing on his four strong legs,

and waited, his own teeth bared. At the last instant he shifted slightly, presenting his shoulder, but still the stallions hit with a thud Buck could clearly hear. The sound sent an exciting thrill through Buck, and the scream of rage that old Club let out caused a wild trembling inside his chest. A powerful impulse that he did not understand caused him to take a few steps closer, but the sight of the two angry forms circling in the gray dust brought him to a halt.

Suddenly the two shapes shot upward to their full height on their strong hind legs. They were chest to chest, their forefeet churning at each other. They went in close, and Club tilted his head sidewise and shot his widespread jaw with its sharp teeth at his opponent's throat. He found skin and something beneath it, closed his jaws, and twisted them savagely. His teeth cut and scraped, but the hold was not deep enough to do serious damage.

The paint fell back, screaming with pain. He went down on a white-splashed flank, covering it with dust. Club pursued him grimly, seeking to trample him into the ground. The paint rolled, trying to get out of the way, but Club went over him, the deformed front foot leaving a long scrape across the white-splashed ribs. The effort caused Club to trip, and now he, too, went down, struggling and thrashing in the dust. One of the paint's rear hoofs caught Club in the flank. The younger stallion rolled to his feet quicker than Club, but Club was up a second later, bellowing with rage. He charged, head thrusting out from his heavy neck like a snake's, teeth bared. The paint stallion saw this vicious determined onslaught coming, and turned and fled. It was his first bunch of mares and his first serious fight, and he had had all the punishment he could take.

Club pursued the paint but, suffering from his own hurts, soon lost ground. Satisfied with the victory, he came to a halt and stood watching his opponent with glowering eyes.

The paint kept going until he was certain he was out of

danger, then slowed, turned, and stopped. Blood was trickling from the cut on his neck, and blood and dust had turned the white splash on his ribs dark. This meant little to him, however. It was the loss of his band that brought the hurt unhappy whinny from his throat. But his mares had already mingled with those of Club's band and paid no attention. Stallion fights were stallion business, and mares accepted the winner as a matter of course.

Buck felt a kinship with the defeated horse and moved through the brush toward him. Engrossed in watching Club and the mares, the paint did not notice Buck until the big yearling was quite close. Then he swung his gaze around. His head was covered with dust, and his eyes were dull with weariness.

Buck, younger and having recently received similar treatment, halted, timid and unsure of himself. He was by no means certain that this black-and-white stallion would not attack him. But at the moment the paint had had all the fight he wanted. Now he was looking for peace, and there really was nothing for him and the young yellow newcomer to fight about. Neither of them had followers or pretensions of range or pride to uphold. Instead they were both outcasts, at the bottom of a wild band's social regard.

The paint made the first move, coming through the brush toward Buck, his manner entirely peaceful. He extended his dark nose, and Buck responded meekly to be sure there could be no misunderstanding. There was no threatening or bluster. Both horses were reassured and pleased by the other's company. Buck presently knew he was hungry and began to eat. A short time later the paint reached for a grass clump, too. When he moved there was a visible stiffness in one of his hind legs where old Club had stepped on it.

The old red stallion, judging his victory to be now complete, turned and made his way back to the mares and colts. His presence was accepted but caused no excitement. He, in turn, was indifferent to them, now that the question of ownership had been settled. They would, he knew, stay together if undisturbed. The only thing he had to worry about was the arrival of another covetous stallion.

Near nightfall the mares went to a creek in the bottom to drink. Buck and his companion out in the brush noticed this movement and immediately ceased grazing to follow. This brought an uplifted head and a sullen stare from Club, causing the two young stallions to halt at a respectful distance. Seeing this, Club turned and ambled on after the band.

Buck and the paint kept the others in sight until it was completely dark. Then they spent the night in the brush near each other, knowing they would see the band in the morning.

10

The paint was three years old. That he had managed to have a band of his own so young was the result of good luck. Some hard running by men a few weeks earlier had scattered a wild bunch, and the paint ranging alone, after having been run out of his own home band, had been the first stallion to encounter this little group. Naturally he had assumed possession as bunch stallion, a position which he had soon lost to old Club. Now again alone, he was in the same status as his younger companion, and as the days passed, they developed a somewhat fixed pattern of existence.

By staying on the fringe of Club's band, they managed to maintain a partial relationship, which satisfied at least some of their herd instincts. This brought them, however, under the almost daily scrutiny of old Club, who was constantly on watch and unrelenting in his distrust of them. He tolerated their presence only as long as they did not get too close. When they came nearer than he liked, he immediately came limping in their direction with flattened ears. This invariably made them halt, which resulted in Club's halting, too, since he had made his point. None of them could find any reason for pressing on to a fight that would have a predictable result and change nothing. It was a situation they had to accept, so they made the best of it, found enough to eat, and put flesh on their young bones.

It seemed that this might have gone on indefinitely when in

midsummer there was a new development. Another animal joined them; it just appeared at the crest of a ridge and, after a brief survey, came down and moved in. This stranger was mild-mannered, but did not act as if it was his habit to ask permission for whatever he wanted to do. His head was big, and his ears were long and hairy. His color was a tawny gray, with dark, almost black lower legs and small round hoofs that were completely sure on the rocks. He was a burro—a wild one—smaller even than Buck, and his being alone indicated that his situation was probably similar to theirs—he, too, was an outcast, probably as the result of a fight with one of his own kind. At any rate, he evidenced a need for companionship and stayed with Buck and the paint. They soon found him comfortable to have around.

Old Club, however, regarded this male newcomer with the same dislike that he showed for the two young horses and appeared at the fringe of the bunch whenever the burro came too near. He never charged him, and the little burro, in turn, never pressed the issue or caused trouble. He soon became the accepted third member of the little banished group, as permanent as almost anything could be in that world of constant conflict and change.

Things settled down in the wild bunch. There was only the usual bickering among the mares regarding choice grass or siesta spots. Club kept aloof from this, and no other stud appeared to challenge his position. Nor did there happen to be in the band any other young male of an age and physical development to arouse the old stallion's jealousy. All this peace and calm was good as it permitted the horses to store up flesh and strength for the coming winter.

They filled their bellies with the hard but nutritious browse of the high slopes. Following the knowing lead mare, they made their way over the passes to the crumbly twisted river bottoms.

The best of the forage here was taken by white-faced cattle during the summer, but even so, after the ranchers had driven their cows to the lower fields, it was the only wintering range available to many of the wild bands. Sometimes during severe winters the horses found it difficult to survive.

Buck and the little group of outcasts trailed along behind the bunch, as faithful to it and the old leader as if they had been permitted to be regular members.

The first snow came while they were still on the slopes, but they were in the protected bottoms when winter hit with a vengeance, blizzard winds whipping the high country with stinging burdens of sleet and snow. This was followed by bitter cold, which turned the surface of the still pools of water to ice. Food was hard to find, and even the horses' thick winter hair did not entirely hide their protruding hip bones. Old Club relaxed his jealousy enough to permit the little band of misfits to huddle closer at night with the others for mutual warmth. The misery was too bitter for fighting.

When the fitful storm finally blew itself out and the sun came again, they set out in the middle of the cold short days to search for food in earnest. In this they were joined by the big-eared mule deer who had waited out the bad weather in the protection of the nearby brush.

The juniper and the mountain mahogany had already been browsed on high up, but Buck saw the deer standing on their hind legs to reach still higher. He tried to do so, too, with some success, and so did the sturdy burro, but most of the horses sought out what low bushes they could find in the rocky pockets and up the steep short ravines.

Others gnawed the willows and cottonwood-tree bark. Almost nothing they could get into their mouths and chew was rejected. Still their flanks became hollow, and layers of flesh disappeared from their ribs. But their long winter coats conserved the heat in their bodies, and only two of Club's bunch were lost. Both of these were old mares weakened by age as well as hunger. One simply lay down and did not get up again; the other, seeking water, broke through the ice close to the bank, and was swept into a deep pool where she drowned.

11

Spring came at last, and the band slowly fed its way up the soft crumbly slopes. They nibbled hungrily at the pale grass in the pockets and folds. It kept them alive but did not give them much strength. The sun, though bright, brought little warmth to the cold ground. The horses searched for grass and browse almost constantly during the daylight hours. Finally, on the long south slopes, the earth began to mellow. The grass grew faster, and the horses could fill out their hollow flanks. Old Club again eyed the young stallions and the burro with jealous warning, causing them to form their own little group apart from the others. Once more they were outcasts. The burro had wintered with the bunch and seemed content to stay. He and Buck were inclined to regard the paint, who was older and bigger, as their leader, though most of the time their existence was merely a matter of trailing after the band, following wherever it went.

Buck was now a strong and wiry two-year-old. He could climb the steep slopes as swiftly as any, and was agile and surefooted in the rocks. His coat was a strong yellow, and a light brown stripe ran from his withers to the root of his tail. His mane and tail were a slightly darker shade of yellow, and his lower legs were brown, almost black. Many horsemen would call him a dun, but not all would agree.

The days became long, warm, and lazy. The grass grew thick and strong. Buck and his two companions fattened, and Buck added a full inch and a half to his height. His new coat was bright and silky. The grit on the slopes ground his hoofs back to the soles and made them tough. He moved with a tireless springy step. He no longer whinnied when he saw the bulky shape of his foster mother grazing among the others.

Horsemen came late that summer and pushed the wild band back to the higher ridges, away from the fields and fences. Another time two persons walking dogged them all one day but never got close. An old lone stud appeared one morning and tried to steal some mares. Club spotted him immediately, and attacked with such ferocity that the fight was soon over. Limping from his bruises, the stranger went back in the direction he had come. Otherwise the summer was calm and peaceful, and when night frosts began to bring red and yellow colors to the creeks and ravines, the bunch went back to the winter country.

The winter was not so severe, and the horses came through in better condition than in the previous year. Buck, now nearing three years of age, wintered fat and was nearly as big as the paint. There were four outcasts now; another big yearling, dark brown in color, had joined the group in the late spring. His presence caused hardly any change in their habits except requiring a little farther ranging for the preferred food.

They were back on the summer range, on the side of the sprawling Owyhee range, when early one afternoon there came a strange sound, a thin high-pitched whine, distant and faint. This was something they had heard before, but it had never been as long and persistent. After the first intent pause, Buck returned to grazing and gave little attention to the noise. Then he became aware that it was increasing and rapidly coming nearer. Some of the older horses were showing definite nervousness; the bay lead mare had her head up and was rolling her eyes at the sky. A few seconds later, she whirled and started moving at the long trot she used when she was certain there was danger.

The others picked up the movement, and the old stallion clumped to his usual place at the end of the line. Buck and his companions followed. Buck looked around, expecting to see a horseman somewhere, but did not find one. Nor did Club send back his customary trumpeting challenge. Up front the lead mare increased her gait to a gallop. Buck knew something was threatening. Then, suddenly, the noise became an ear-splitting scream that seemed to be bearing down almost on top of him. It was so unexpected and startling that it made him cower involuntarily, and during that second, almost deafening his ears, it swept past and on into the wide valley.

It took Buck an instant to recover, and he saw that the other horses about him were cowering, too. Then all seemed to collect themselves at once, and there was wild leaping and confusion. In front and below, Buck got a glimpse of the bay lead mare, turning her high head about as if for once not certain of which way to go. Nearer Club had his strong old legs braced in stubborn defiance.

Buck and his outcast companions moved nearer, less afraid now of the old stallion. Then the noise stilled them again. Thin and shrill, it was returning. Above a nearby ridge there was a sudden appearance, something sweeping into view. It looked like a giant bird with strange wide wings, and a thin silvery circle of light where the head should have been. It turned down toward them, and the screaming sound came again.

The lead mare sprang into action, no longer uncertain. She raced down the basin, and the others followed, not in the usual disciplined line but in helter-skelter flight. Buck, the paint, the yearling, and the burro went, too, leaping the low bushes. They went past Club, who was looking back over his shoulder.

The sound became still shriller, but with an undertone of roaring thunder. It was close behind. Buck leaped recklessly ahead, moving in among the mares and colts. The scream was above them, on them . . . inside their ears. The running horses split in all directions. Suddenly there was no way to go, no escape. Buck was terrified, more frightened than he had ever been in his life. He locked his legs and came to a cowering halt. Then the thing was past, going on, taking its awful noise with it.

It was the first time Buck had ever had the experience of being run by an airplane, but the method was used occasionally in rough areas where running on horseback was unusually difficult. Knowing and daring pilots could by repeated passes herd the wild bands from the slopes and ravines down to flatter areas where riders on grain-hardened horses could take over, either roping the animals or sometimes even driving whole bunches into prepared traps. Such assaults from above were so new that the horses did not know how to cope with them.

Old Club, however, had been run before by airplane several times. Like the other horses, he was afraid. But with the handicap of his clubbed foot he could not scramble around over the rocks and through the scrub timber as quickly, so he had been cornered twice. The first time he had cowered in fear; the second time he had turned and faced the big thing. It had not struck him, as he had feared, but had flashed past over his head.

In the rocks he was limping at the tail of the bunch when the airplane completed another wide circle out over the valley, climbed to altitude that would clear the high timbered ridge, and banked into the upper end of the basin. The band—mares and colts and all—was far below, dots of color against the green brush and gray shale.

For this pass, the pilot throttled back his engine and dipped the nose down in a long glide. The decrease in noise caused the horses to remain still longer than before. They waited, frightened and poised. The plane skimmed low between the ridges. The rumble of the engine increased slightly as the pilot edged up his power.

Club, uppermost of the bunch, climbed to the crest of a great round boulder, half buried in the ground near the middle of the basin. As the plane hurtled down, he turned to face it.

Buck, ready to run, watched the old stallion. As the engine sound increased, the Roman-nosed old horse slowly reared, lifting his front hoofs. The plane rushed on, lower still in its glide. It looked as if it might strike the red form. Club's front legs cut the air in long determined gestures of defiance. His nose was up, and his old yellow fangs were bared to strike.

The plane whipped on, overhead. A new sound, a single sharp pop, could be heard above the noise of the engine. Then came a great and sudden roaring as the pilot put on a surge of full power to pull out of the glide.

The bunch panicked in fear, scattering wildly. As Buck turned, he noticed that Club did not seem frightened. The great red-hued horse was lowering back to all fours, his movement slow and strangely awkward. The two big rock-battered front hoofs touched the rough surface of the boulder, and then the powerful form lost its strength and wilted. Suddenly it collapsed; the red body sprawled on the rock.

Buck started to wheel and run with the others, but the old stallion's actions seemed very strange to him, because with the band running he knew old Club would have died on his feet before lying down. That is what had happened; Club had been killed by a high-powered rifle bullet from the low-flying airplane.

12

Many wild horses have been shot, for many different reasons. Many stallions are killed because they are pests, breaking down fences and molesting tame mares. Others, including mares and colts, are shot to rid the range of them, usually so that the grass, as meager as it is, can be grazed by beef cattle.

Old Club was shot because he was in the way of the runners in the plane. By his defiant actions he was making it more difficult for them to achieve their purpose. So they shot him. That is why men in runner-planes often carry high-powered rifles, sometimes buckshot-loaded shotguns. Old crippled studs are of small value anyway, even to the canneries.

Buck waited no longer before racing after the scattered band, which was now running over a rounded rocky shoulder. He leveled down, soon caught up, and made his way forward until he was among the frightened mares and colts. The old bay mare, his foster mother, was off to the right, on the lower side, with the filly, now two years old, galloping easily behind her. From long habit when he was uneasy, Buck angled down toward the mare.

The bunch was weary and soon slowed. They looked around and were reassured. Some darted their heads down for quick mouthfuls of grass. There were a few minutes or so of relaxing, and then the drone of the airplane began to increase. It became louder. The horses began to eye the sky and shake their heads nervously. The sound grew swiftly in volume. The foals—suck-ling and yearling alike—huddled close to their mothers. The old lead mare turned, trying to pinpoint the noise from its echo against the steeply rising slope.

A few seconds later the silvery plane appeared above the ridge, its roar becoming suddenly full-throated. It sailed out against the blue sky, then banked sharply and headed down. This assault from the sky was beyond the horses' understanding. The thin circle of the propeller seemed to point directly at them. Finally they broke in panic and fled, not in any order but in desperate flight.

Buck saw the great upright ears of the burro and turned his course toward them. Nothing seemed to excite the little jack very much; he was always calm and reassuring. Now he ran with steady stride on his round surefooted hoofs. Buck swung in behind him. The shrill screaming somewhere in back of them was increasing.

The old red mare, still followed by her last offspring, was running to their right, a little lower on the rocky ledge. Two other mares were in front of them, one with a suckling foal.

The airplane screeched above them, so close the noise seemed to split their ears. The rocks beneath their feet seemed to tremble. Buck laid his ears back against his neck and ran with all his might, guided by the big upright ears in front. With a maddening blast of air and sound, the plane was above them; then it went past, carrying its noise with it. Buck could see it, rapidly becoming smaller in the air out over the valley.

The burro swung to the left. Buck followed closely, without hesitation. He discovered they were running near the rim of a steep cliff and, looking, did not see any of the mares and foals that had been below them on the right. In that instant of desperate fear they had disappeared.

The burro slowed and halted, near the rim. Looking down,

Buck could see the broken rock of the slope and the pointed tops of the young trees. Ragged trails of dust rose from places along the slope.

Panting heavily, Buck welcomed the chance to blow. The burro was breathing deeply, too. He was motionless otherwise for some time. The sound of the plane became faint, then started to increase. The old lead mare and the others with her on the slope above became still and intent, too, their dark shapes clear to Buck against the blue sky.

The dust trails below the rim drifted into the crowns of the evergreens; no other movement was visible below. The burro raised his head, and his big ears swiveled around like scoops. The airplane sound continued to increase.

Buck waited, uncertain and shaken by all this recent terror. The noise of the airplane became louder, swiftly drawing nearer. From her place up on the crown of the rocky shoulder, the old lead mare stamped her hoofs and snorted. The others moved toward her, obviously seeking reassurance. She took a few steps into a fringe of juniper at one side of the rock and halted. The others followed quickly and gathered about her.

Hoof steps sounded close to Buck. He found the burro was moving along the rim, and hurried to catch up. The little jackass picked his way over the loose boulders carefully. He soon came to a break in the rim, a small crevice cluttered with shale and occasional little stunted bushes that led downward. Buck would never have considered trying this descent, but the burro after a second's survey stepped down on the shale. There was some sliding but not much. The burro went on with short stiff steps.

Buck still hesitated, doubtful. The shale was loose; the angle was sharp, and farther down, there was a sheer fall of a dozen feet or more. But the burro kept going; Buck knew that he would not turn back. And the air above was beginning to tremble once more with the sound of the airplane.

Buck's feet were more awkward than the burro's. The gray shale slipped and tumbled about him, but he made steady progress. Soon he was close to his companion's short tail.

At the lower end of the crevice, the burro turned along a steep wall, digging his small hoofs into the accumulated dirt of a crack. Buck had no choice except to follow. They made it to another downward crevice, not as bad as the first. At the bottom of this, however, there was a vertical fall of several feet. The burro paused, then leaped down, landing so easily Buck was encouraged. The burro went on with quick sliding steps on what obviously was good footing.

The airplane roared above them. Buck jumped. He fell when he hit, but it did not hurt, and he was able to catch his footing after the first roll.

Below the little gray animal slanted his big ears backward to help himself balance on the steep descent. Soon he was at the foot of it, where the earth sloped outward more gently. Slipping and sliding, Buck started a small cascade of rocks before reaching that point. The burro had moved on. The scream of the airplane was dwindling.

The burro paused, for a look upward at the cliff, then turned along the base of it, moving leisurely now. The noise of the airplane was only a distant drone.

They had gone some distance when Buck saw a big bulk on the ground ahead. It was still and silent, but there was something familiar about it. When the burro reached it, he lowered his white nose and sniffed. Buck saw then that it was the old red mare, his foster mother. He pushed forward to nudge her in recognition, and found that her body was coated heavily with the gray dust of the hillside. Her old worn body was still warm, but it did not move. There was no sound of breathing, and the bony rounded bridge of her nose had been crushed inward by some powerful blow. Buck looked about for the young filly, but she was nowhere to be seen.

There was a sound of threshing about not far away in the dense stiff growth. Buck and the burro went toward it, close to the base of the long decline. There in a little cavity of her own making, they found one of the two mares that had been in front of the foster mother. She, too, had plunged over the rim and was now covered with the dust of her fall. Her head was up, and when she saw them, she struggled to get her legs under her, but the rear ones were useless. Twice she half rose, only to fall back both times. Then she quit trying but neighed plaintively when later in the afternoon Buck and the burro left to graze.

The airplane did not come again that day. Buck and the burro found good grass along the base of the bluff and, comfortably filled, spent the night there. In the morning they grazed again and near midday went back to where they had found the two mares. The old foster mother had not moved, and there was neither neighing nor threshing in the stiff brush where they had left the other one. When they went to the small cavity, the gray form of a coyote leaped out of it, its muzzle bloody. The quick burro helped it on its way with a one-footed kick in the ribs as it passed.

They saw nothing of the third mare or the suckling foal, but while they were at the spot, they were surprised by a happy eager neigh and turned to see the red filly come trotting through the aspens that lined the bottom of the slope. Buck recognized her and replied to the greeting. They rubbed noses. The burro regarded them with big calm eyes. Nothing excited him very much.

In some manner the filly had survived the fall over the rim. She was coated with thick dust, and there was a scraped place on her ribs where she had hit a rock or something, but otherwise she was unharmed; she did not even limp.

The burro turned and started along the upturn, and the filly made certain she would not be left behind by hurrying after him. Buck brought up the rear.

It was a strange-looking group: the long-eared jackass, the wiry, yellow three-year-old stallion, and the smooth red filly, visibly not belonging to either of the other two. A common need for companionship held them together. Even the burro did not wish to be alone, and at the time there were very few of his own kind in the Owyhees, those that there were being the descendants of escapees from early miners and prospectors. For the first few days the filly would not let Buck out of her sight, sensing that he was more akin to her than was the burro. Buck in turn was generally more relaxed and content when she was nearby.

For days they roamed like this, the three of them, along the rocky lower ridges of the sprawling mountain range. They searched out pockets of grass, browsed on the gray-green slopes of sage, and drank from clear springs or trickling creeks. Usually when they moved, the burro was in front, his big ears stiffly upright as he watched the country ahead. Both Buck and the filly followed willingly. While not big for her age, the filly was bright-eyed and lively.

One afternoon weeks later, after going through a saddle in one of the ridges, the burro came to a sudden halt, and his great ears swiveled forward. Buck, quickly pushing up beside the gray shape, saw that there were red and dark forms on the slope beyond—horses. Up went Buck's head, and an eager whinny sounded from his throat. Then he took the lead at a long trot down the slope.

The horses raised their heads for a long questioning look, then resumed grazing—with one exception. This one was a young black, a stallion. Buck kept watch for a second stallion, perhaps an older one, but saw none. It was a small band—three mares, two with suckling foals—besides the stud. The stud, Buck knew, would be pretty certain sooner or later to give him trouble.

Buck, the burro, and the filly, all three approached the bunch. The filly was very happy and went in among the mares without any hesitation. One of the mares nosed her briefly, then returned to grazing. Buck and the burro approached more cautiously and halted a short distance away.

It was the black's first band, and he was not quite sure of himself, but the displeasure of the situation continued to boil inside him until he could stand it no longer. It was his bunch, and he would not tolerate these newcomers anymore. Putting his ears back flat, he charged, his neck arched out. Luckily for Buck perhaps, the black selected his nearest target, which was the donkey. This proved to be a big mistake.

For all their apparent apathy, members of this four-footed family are exceedingly quick and rugged. The burro did not move, until the stallion was only about a length away. Then, with lightning-like speed, the slab-sided little gray creature switched ends. Having already gauged the range, his small round hoofs began to beat a rapid tattoo on the black's forelegs and chest. The blows were so swift and so accurate that the young stallion recoiled in a daze. One hard lick of hoof followed another, with hardly a break in the timing. This was something the young black had never before encountered. Horses normally fight as much with their teeth as their heels—often even more. Horses fight, too, by something like innings, with rest periods in between. But not this small creature.

The stallion gave ground, backing. His big-eared opponent continued to pursue him, and what a pursuit! Coming hind end first like a crab, his legs a blur of motion, the burro kept pounding the young stallion's shoulders, ribs, rump, and anything else within range. Bam! Bam! The hard hoofs landed again and again, leaving their rounded marks in the dust on the black hide. This routed the stallion completely. He gave up all attempt at fighting and lined out for the brush.

The burro halted. He watched the flight of his recent opponent a few seconds, then shook himself, lowered his bony head, and began eating as if nothing unusual had happened. The black, at a safe distance, wheeled and came to a stop but gave no indication that he wanted to return. The beating he had just received was one he would remember a long time.

So it was that Buck, without having proffered even so much of a threat as laying his ears back, found himself the stallion of a bunch. That pleased him, made him feel more important, but after that demonstration of cool courage and fighting ability, he stayed a discreet distance from Big Ears until it became apparent that the little burro had no desire to take over a horse band, though male jackasses have been known to do so.

13

The new bunch contained a trim young mare with dark spots on her white rump—an appaloosa as the ranchers would call her. Her eyes were sharp and her courage was strong, and she proved to be the leader. Whenever she started, the others followed. Wherever she went, they went, too, including Buck and the burro. Organization of the bunch was complete; it had a leader and a stallion and mares and colts, not many but enough. And it had something extra—the jackass.

For a few days the ousted black lurked in the distance, hopeful it would seem of making a successful return. Then he disappeared, apparently deciding to seek a band in which there were no long ears.

Buck assumed his duty of watchfulness. That was the position he had been born for, to detect and fight away any strange stallions. And he did a good job. When the band moved, he took up his position in the rear, for that was the direction from which dangers were most likely to appear. Also, back there, he could loaf along as he wished. Stallions do not like to be pushed or annoyed by romping foals. The burro was usually back in that area, too, and when the flies were at their worst these two would sometimes stand head to tail, switching the insects off each other.

It was not long before autumn came, and no strange horses,

with or without riders, had appeared to test Buck's alertness and ability. The days shortened, and the spotted mare began to edge away from the higher land. When the harsh days of winter came, they were back in the protection of deep twisted canyons.

As usual, cattle had been there, leaving the evidence in round patties of dried manure under the trees, where in summer there had been shade, and along the creek banks. The grass was short; the ranchers wanted the stock to get all of it. In some places the ground was bare, badly overgrazed. Not much was left for the horses, but they had nowhere else to go. The cows were now pastured down in the fields, among the haystacks, where the appearance of wild horses would bring men on the run. So the band ate cottonwood bark and willow leaves and twigs in the isolated river breaks.

They were hardy and accustomed to searching sedulously for their food. They were agile and sure-footed, able to go into the pockets and up the rocky ravines where the big-bodied cattle could not go. They could exist on the tough stunted browse and join the mule deer in standing on their hind legs under the wide mahogany trees.

Other horse bands wintered in that far-flung broken country too, most of them small, sometimes numbering not more than four or five, because that was all the scarce feed would support. They ranged wide, and mostly kept apart. Since it was not the breeding season, the stallions were not so prone to fight. They also needed to use their energy on the rigorous hunting for food.

When spring arrived, all Buck's band were still alive and able to travel, except one young mare. During a frigid period, she had tried to cross a frozen slope and fallen. The slide carried her out of sight below, and she did not return.

The spotted mare led them back to summer range where they found the grass plentiful and nutritious. All of the high shaded snowbanks had not disappeared when she gave birth to a little spotted foal, and within two hours' time, it was trotting by her side.

Buck had a birthday, too, though he did not know it. One bright warm afternoon he entered the fifth year of his life. At four, he was almost fully mature and prepared to meet all the responsibilities of a wild stallion.

During the next two weeks two other mares of Buck's little band had colts, too. The third mare, a little buckskin less than two years old, did not. In all, not counting the new colts but including the burro, who had wintered with them, there were nine in the bunch when a month or so later a strange horse appeared.

Buck moved a few steps in this horse's direction to send out a warning to stay away. The horse stopped, and then Buck saw that there was a man on its back. Immediately old memories came inside him—disturbing memories of hard pounding hoofs and swinging loops of rope. He repeated the warning, bringing the whole band to attention. A few seconds later the strange horse moved, advancing on through the low brush.

Buck let out another indignant cry.

The spotted mare snorted her distrust, turned, and headed up the opposite slope. Buck watched to see what effect this would have on the strange horse and rider and found that it caused no change. He turned then and followed the band.

All the rest of that day the horseman kept after them, mostly at a walk. He never got very close, but he never stopped nor permitted them to stop, either. He knew very well what he was doing, wearing them out by keeping them moving, without any time to eat or much time to drink. And back at a camp beside a creek in a small ravine, there were two more riders to help him. Buck, of course, knew nothing of that, but these men meant business, and it was Buck they were after.

They worked downcountry for a wealthy rancher, who having seen Buck and the band at a distance, had decided he wanted the wild yellow stud. He had not been in the country long and knew little about wild horses, but that did not stop him from sending up his men.

That night, when welcome darkness descended on the dry harsh land and the wild band could stop, the mares stood with drooped tired heads, and the little foals lay down almost at once. It had been a long hard day, and their hoofs were sore from all the traveling.

Buck's hoofs were worn thin, too, but he did not lie down, not that night. He stayed on his feet and kept alert, listening to the sounds.

Early the next morning the horseman—actually another one—reappeared and set the bunch in motion. The spotted mare took the lead, following the same trail up the shale she always took when leaving that area. The man on horseback did not alter his gait, but he nodded his head in satisfaction. The wild horses were being driven in the direction the runners wished them to take.

Unaware of this, the appaloosa mare in the lead went over the top of the ridge and down the trail on the opposite side, traveling at a long walk, which was as fast as she wished to go on her sore feet. She kept to the trail, too, to avoid the sharp rocks. Two of the mares in the line behind her limped noticeably.

In the bottom the trail turned downward and a quarter of a mile or so farther on entered a narrow but steep-walled little canyon beside a merrily running creek. The lead mare moved steadily, not bothering to look behind. She knew the band was following, with the burro and Buck in the rear, and there was no doubt in her mind that the runner was somewhere in back of them, as he had been all the previous day. Below the canyon and over the ridge to the right, there was a meadow with good grass, and that was the goal in her mind.

Buck, who was certain of the location of the pursuing rider, had halted and watched the man come over the ridge crest on his strong-legged horse. Out of the corners of his eyes he could see him now and then back along the trail. The man was in no hurry; still he never stopped. The burro went along steadily in front of Buck, his great ears pointed straight up as usual.

The lead mare reached the end of the little canyon where the trail, passing close to a high rock shoulder, entered a wider flat area on this side of the creek. The brush was low and sparse, and the trail lay straight for some distance. The leader paused to nibble the tip of a limb, but went on before the mare behind her caught up.

One by one, they entered the flat. The last small foal, red like most of the band, went past the rock shoulder, two or three small strides behind its mother. The burro was next. Suddenly, as he reached the shoulder, his left ear swiveled about, and an instant later he spun on his heels and ran back.

Buck halted, his eyes wide with amazement at this swift action. The burro was running straight at him, and when the burro ran, there was good reason for it. The reason emerged from behind the rock shoulder, a second later—two men on horses. They had been waiting in ambush, had let the band pass undisturbed, and intended to let the burro go by also. But his sharp ears had caught some sound, and when he wheeled, the men had charged, knowing their presence had been discovered. They came fast, long loops of rope dangling from their right hands. Beyond them the frightened mares and colts ran, too, in the opposite direction.

Buck knew the danger instantly and pivoted on his heels back into the narrow canyon. Before he had gone far, the pursuing rider appeared in front of him, closer than he had expected. This man had the loop of rope in motion around his big hat. Buck was forced to halt; he could not go past. He turned on his heels again—and collided with the little jackass, who had been running close behind him.

The blow knocked them both off balance. Buck struggled to keep from going into the creek, where the water was shallow but fast. Then something closed swiftly about his head and hit him a hard and stunning blow, jerked his head high, and began to choke him. Panic rushed up inside him. He fought and struggled with all his strength, rearing on his hind legs, placing all his weight against the pull. But it would not give, and the loop around his throat kept drawing tighter and tighter. Black spots danced briefly before his eyes and merged. He could not see. He felt himself falling and heard a crash that somehow did not seem to involve him. A second later he was unconscious.

14

These men were old hands. They knew their business. When Buck regained consciousness, there was a strong leather halter on his head. He was lying on the ground near the creek, not yet knowing just what had happened. He was afraid to move because of that strange thing on his head. Then he heard an odd and new sound—human voices.

"He's quite a little stud," one voice said.

"Yeah," another replied, "but I don't know if he's going to be worth all the time and hard riding."

"He will be to the boss, I guess. He thinks he might get some good colts from him, thinks they should be quick and tough, good in the mountains. It's his idea."

There was a grunt; then the second voice said, "What the boss don't know about wild mustangs would fill a book, a big one. I bet this is the only wild stud he ever saw, and he was nearly half a mile away then, looking through them big binoculars."

"I've seen some a lot worse. He's not as big as you might like, but there's nothing wrong with the way he's put together. I don't see anything that looks like it might break."

"That's right. And you know the kind of legs and feet these rocks and hills up here develop. You don't have to worry about these horses going lame."

"I'd say he's pretty close to pure mustang, as close as I've seen up here in a long time. The boss don't know what he's getting into. It's all a crazy dream of his."

"Better not let him hear you say that, if you want to keep your job. I'd guess it's about the best you've had in quite a while."

Just then Buck stiffened his muscles in a hard flounce that lifted him up to his feet, halter and all. He saw two of the men standing close by.

"Hey, he's come to," one said.

"Yeah. Look out!"

Buck was running by that time, headed down the canyon. A second later he received another hard shocking blow, this one across his nose. It jerked him around so hard he landed sprawl-legged. He felt strong pressure against the back of his neck as well as on his nose and saw a straight hard rope stretched to a stunted tree.

"Take it easy," one of the men said. "Don't break your fool neck. That's the trouble with these hard heads; they don't know when to quit. If anything happened to him, the boss would can us all."

"He might, at that. Let's get him down to the truck. I'll feel better when he's in a corral, all in one piece."

"What about the donkey? What'll we do with him?"

"Take him, too. We might as well since we've got a rope on him. We're lucky there. He's not branded, but he's broke to lead. Somebody has had him before."

The pressure behind Buck's ears became maddening. He suddenly leaped forward, past the stunted tree. He thought he was free. But at the end of two more leaps the hard blow hit him across the nose, jerking him around again.

"It's a good thing we've got that halter on him," a man said, "or we wouldn't have much chance. In a loop, he'd choke himself to death in no time. Call Tom to bring the jack."

The other man went toward the rock shoulder and yelled, and a minute later the third man appeared, leading the little burro. Buck's ears pricked forward at the sight. The burro followed the man calmly. Buck eased his weight against the relentless pull of the rope.

Saddled horses were standing nearby. A man went to one of them, lifted a stirrup, and tightened the cinch. "The jack can be a help to us," he said. "They've been running together." He mounted the horse, rode closer, and another man untied Buck's rope from the tree and handed the end of it to the rider.

Then began the worst experience Buck had ever had in his life. The halter tightened behind his ears, and the rope pulled him forward. He stood it until his hoofs were sliding, then went into a bucking jumping frenzy, going every which way and doing anything and everything in a desperate effort to get free. The man on the ground got out of the way, and the one on horseback kept turning his mount to keep the rope taut. Buck bucked into the stunted tree, went past it, turned back, and found his head snubbed so tight against the trunk he could hardly move it.

"Bring the jack up beside him," the man on the horse said. "Maybe that'll calm him down some."

The nearness of the burro did help. Buck ceased his frantic struggling. When he was untangled and the burro moved forward, led by one of the riders, Buck followed him, but only a few steps before halting. Immediately the pressure behind his ears increased, and in spite of his resistance he was pulled forward. After a time he learned that holding back was useless.

It took a long time and a lot of pulling and pushing and yelling before Buck was finally in a big truck with other horses and the burro. It was late in the afternoon. Buck was almost completely exhausted, but beside him the burro's big ears were standing as straight up as ever. Their presence gave Buck much needed reassurance during the long noisy ride in the night that followed.

Still, when the truck finally came to a stop and the floor beneath his hoofs quit shaking, the yellow stallion was practically numb with fright and weariness.

After more pushing and pulling and being yelled at, Buck found himself alone in a dark high-fenced pen. It was a great relief to him to be on solid earth once more. It was a relief, too, when all the banging and the other strange and irritating noises faded away and left them alone. Still Buck knew things were not right. He made a trip of inspection around the fence, which seemed to him to be high black walls, and found there were no openings. The burro did not seem worried and soon went to sleep, but Buck paced the walls for some time longer before he settled down.

It was a high strong pen, built especially to hold stallions. The fence was made of weathered vertical planks, almost solid, with only small cracks between the boards. On one side was a good three-walled shelter that had a big hay manger, a grain box, and in one corner a water container. The solid back wall had a window through which feed could be passed. It also had a door, though this was not then apparent to Buck. None of the pen's former occupants had been pets.

The manger had hay in it, and when the burro awoke, he went to it and began to eat. Buck had never eaten any hay before, but he was hungry, and with the burro's example, it did not take long for him to find out what it was like. It was green and sweet-smelling, and in the early morning light they ate, side by side, until it was all gone, going to the container regularly for sips of water. The burro settled himself in a sunny corner for more sleep, but Buck was restless and uneasy. There was much about this that he did not like. He made another inspection of the fence and found a place where he could, with one eye, look through the cracks between the planks.

Outside he could see other corrals, but these were made of

spaced horizontal boards, less high than the vertical ones that surrounded him. In some of these corrals he could see horses, eating or resting. He whinnied at them, but they paid no attention.

Beyond there was a tall windmill, with a wheel turning at its top. On the ground nearby, water lapped over the edge of a big round watering trough that held many gallons. There was a barn, a big hay shed, and some smaller sheds. Beyond these stood a house, nearly as big as the barn, surrounded by tall green trees. All the buildings and fences were painted white. Trucks stood near the sheds, and a number of bright shiny cars were parked close to the white house. A bull with white on its face and along the top of its neck waddled across the packed ground and drank from the watering trough.

A screeching sound behind caused Buck to start. He looked around and saw that the window in the back wall of the three-sided shelter in his pen was opening. A moment later hay was pushed through this window and allowed to fall into the manger beneath. The burro opened his eyes lazily and watched, too. More hay was pushed through until the manger was well filled. Then the window closed. Buck heard the footsteps of a man moving behind the wall. The burro went over and began to eat. Buck waited a few minutes, then went to the manger, also. The hay was good, but it was difficult for him to overcome his distrust.

They were still eating when another sound made Buck turn from the hay quickly. There was an opening in the high fence, and two men were coming through it. On their heads were big hats. They stopped and closed the gate behind them, and stood looking at Buck and the burro.

"You're the foreman," one of them said after a few seconds, "but this business of having a mustang stud on a purebred ranch like this seems a little screwy to me."

"I know," the other one replied, "but it's what the boss wants."

"Why? He's got horses here that cost big money."

"It's an idea he's got."

"When he gets back and takes a close look at this stud, he might change his mind. We can hope so anyway. They don't look as good down in a corral as they do running wild up on a ridge. If I know anything, this fellow won't be easy to break."

"The boss don't want him broke, he wants him 'tamed.' Don't you remember what he said?"

"All right—tamed. Either way, it's liable to be a big waste of time. When'll he be back?"

"A couple of months yet. It's his time; he's paying for it."

"Well, there's no use bustin' our necks about it now. We've got him . . . that's what's important, isn't it?"

The foreman nodded. "Yes."

"What'll we do about the jack?"

"Let him stay in here . . . for the time being" was the answer.

Then the two men turned and left.

After they had gone, Buck went over to the place in the wall where they had stood and tried to find the opening, but it was not there.

15

That day passed, and the next one. Someone came and pushed plenty of the good hay through the shed window, and there was always water in the corner trough, but the two men did not come back through the gate in the wall.

The burro did not worry. He ate hay when he wanted it and spent most of the rest of the time sleeping, or at least standing with his eyes closed, in the sun. Buck, however, could not get over his restlessness. He missed the long sunny upland slopes, the bright green of the willows along the creeks, the darker juniper thickets in the ravines, with the soft dust and noonday shade. He missed the strong tangy water of the springs and trickling creeks. Most of all he missed the bunch, the mares and colts scattered in a hillside meadow, feeding on the grass and low bushes. Their presence and movement, their nearness night and day, had kept his world alive.

In the high-walled pen there was none of this; there was no movement, no companionship, not even any need. He was never even really hungry because there was always hay in the manger. The burro helped, just by being there, though he never did much, just ate and slept . . . and got fat. Meat soon covered his ribs.

The gate in the wall did not open again; the men didn't come. The man who came to throw in the hay never stayed long, and all they saw of him were glimpses. The water in the corner trough came through a pipe; they did not know when.

There was activity outside. In the late afternoon they often heard hoofs, cattle bawling around the watering trough. There were men's voices, sometimes shouting and yelling, at other times low and steady.

Buck spent more and more time at the wall, the one next to the corrals. He learned that by positioning one eye near a crack he could see something of what was going on outside. The cracks were of different widths, and he soon knew just where the wider ones were.

During the day the area was busy with men and horses coming and going. Men caught the horses in the pens, led them out to hitchracks, saddled them, and rode away. Later in the afternoon, men came in, sometimes the same ones. Dismounting, they pulled off their dusty saddles and opened the gates for their horses. The horses often drank at the trough and rolled their sweaty backs in the dust before going to the mangers. At first Buck whinnied at them, but they were always too tired or too hungry to answer him.

Cattle came, too, in small bunches usually of threes or fours, sometimes a ponderous bull with them. After drinking at the overflowing brim of the round trough, they would gather in the shade of the windmill during the hot afternoons and, switching flies off with their tails, chew their cuds.

Other than this very little happened. Buck and the burro were left alone in the stallion pen. Men came and went, and now and then one might open the wall door and look in but only briefly. The only thing that could be counted on regularly was the hay thrown through the window above the manger. The man who did this was just a moving shape back of the wall; they never really saw him.

It went on like this for many days. Buck spent hours walking the fence. His feet wore paths in the dust. Other hours were spent looking through the cracks.

The burro was company, but otherwise not much help. He did not care what went on outside. The opening of the door by the men who glanced in did not disturb him. He would merely open his eyes until they were gone. It was hard to tell at times whether he was asleep or awake, except that at night when there was a little stirring in the other corrals his big ears might lop forward a little.

One afternoon the door opened, and three men came in. Two of them had been there before; the third, smaller, more rounded, and smelling of some puzzling fragrance, was a stranger. Their arrival was enough to send Buck into the far corner of the shed, though the burro only raised his eyelids.

The men paused just inside the door, and one said, "There he is, Mr. Gordy. He wasn't easy to catch. The jack was running with his band."

After a moment the smaller man replied, "He's not as big as he looked up on the range. But I like him."

"The feed he's been getting hasn't hurt him any," the third man said.

There was a short space of silence; then the ranch foreman asked, "You still think you'd like to raise some colts from him, Mr. Gordy?"

"Yes," the ranch owner answered. "I know it's an experiment, but I would just like to see what mustang blood crossed with some good breeding will produce. It might surprise us."

Neither of the others replied to that.

"It is pretty late in the fall," the foreman said. "Colts born in the spring seem to do better . . . better weather and grass."

The owner nodded. "We will hold off till after the real cold weather and then mate him to two or three picked mares. I will tell you which ones. It will be real interesting to see what the foals look like. They should have lots of stamina. We might even start a new strain of horses for cow work."

"Yes, sir," the foreman answered.

"Meanwhile see that he gets the best of feed, plenty of grain and everything," the owner ordered. "I hope we can put a little more size on him. A couple of inches at the withers would help."

"Yes, sir," the foreman agreed. "What about the donkey? Do you want anything special done with him?"

"Not just now, but we'll find something. He looks like a good strong jack."

"Yes, sir, he is."

The ranch owner, however, had his eyes back on Buck. "I like him. Yes, I do. This will be an interesting experiment, men." He paused for a look at his wristwatch. "Now, I must get back to the house," he said and went through the wall door.

The other two men stood there several seconds longer, the foreman looking at the ground and rubbing his nose.

"Yes, sir, we just might . . . ," the hired man said presently, mimicking the owner's voice. Then in normal tones he went on, "The trouble is it's been tried a hundred or so times before."

"Yes," the foreman agreed. "But he doesn't know it. Anyway, why not? Good money has been spent on worse projects. *We* might be surprised. Wouldn't that be something?" He grinned.

The other man shrugged. "Yeah, it would."

The foreman became serious. "You heard what he said about feed . . . the hay and grain, didn't you? See to it."

Turning to look at Buck, the hired man chuckled to himself. "Yellow horse, you're in luck," he said. "You won't believe it, but this is going to be the best winter of your life."

16

It *was* a good winter for Buck. For the first time in his life he had all he wanted to eat anytime he wanted it—good, clean sweet-smelling hay and plump grain, with vitamin supplement also. And he bloomed as many range horses in such a situation do. He grew two inches at the withers and put on another hundred pounds of good solid flesh over his hips and ribs. His dark eyes were bright, and his yellow coat had a satiny glint.

The ranch owner was jubilant. "By George, he's doing fine. He looks wonderful—just as I hoped he would. We may really have something here, men."

The foreman and his helper had to agree. "I *am* surprised," the foreman admitted.

"Yeah, but he's still a mustang," the hired hand said. "It just shows what good feed will do. You can't starve them for years without taking something out of them, and you can't put it back in one generation."

But for Buck it also was an exceedingly dull winter. Nothing happened. The burro was there, of course, fat and well fed, too. But there were no other horses, no bunches or bands, no steep crumbly walls, no mule deer on their hind legs under wide-spreading juniper trees. Nothing unusual happened in the corrals outside. There were the ranch horses, and the cattle at the trough near the windmill, and sometimes men came with axes to break the ice. Seen through the cracks in the board wall day after day, it was not exciting. Buck's restlessness increased, and his hard dark hoofs wore the path around the walls still deeper.

Then, after the days had become longer and the sun brighter and warmer, something did happen. A man opened the wall door, stepped inside, and closed the door behind him. This sent Buck to the far corner under the shed again. The man paid no attention to Buck but went to the burro. The burro was stolid as usual. The man slipped a leather halter over the big straight-lined head, turned back to the door, and went outside, leading the burro.

It took Buck in his corner a few seconds to realize what had happened, and when he did, he raised his head and let out a high dismayed neigh. The burro was gone; he, Buck, was alone, entirely alone. That must not be. Buck charged out of the shed, neighing his loud complaint. No answer came. Buck could hear hoof sounds beyond the wall. He hurried to a well-known crack and put his eye to it. His restricted vision showed a gray shape moving past a white board fence. While he watched, the burro was led out of sight. Buck went quickly along the wall to another crack, hoping the burro would come in view. He did not. Buck hurried along the wall, looking through the cracks as he came to them. He saw the windmill, the big house, and the sheds, but nothing of the familiar gray form with its big ears.

Suddenly the wiry yellow stallion went into a frenzy of dismay. He charged wildly around the pen, kicking and bucking as hard as he could, his hoofs throwing clods of dirt against the walls, even over them at times. He neighed and screamed; he moaned and groaned. He slipped and fell on a wet spot near the water, but was back on his feet in a bound. He raced in under the shed, and back out again. He cried his great resentment to the sky. There was no indication that anyone or anything heard him or cared.

Gradually Buck's desperation wore itself out. He finally came to a halt, near the center of the pen. His big-jowled head dipped, and sank lower and lower in complete dejection. He was still there an hour or more later when the man who put hay in the manger came and opened the window. He threw in a forkful of hay and a second one. Then he paused, put his head through the window for a closer look at Buck, and said, "Come on. It can't be that bad. You gotta eat something. . . ."

The stallion gave no sign he knew anyone was there. The man looked at him another long moment before he shook his head, adding, "I don't know much about horses, but it looks to me like you've got big problems." He pulled back his head and moved on beyond the wall.

Buck stood as he was, his head still low. It seemed as if his hurt was deeper than he could endure.

Time passed. Evening came with its long shadows. Finally, near dark, there was a sound that brought Buck's head up, slowly at first. It was the soft nicker of a mare to her foal, a call Buck had heard many times in the high mountain meadows. His ears pricked forward, and he listened intently as if uncertain. The nicker came again, low and reassuring.

Buck moved, with soft and cautious steps. He went to the wall crack that looked toward the windmill. There, at the watering trough, were several dark shapes, one plainly smaller than the others. Buck knew they were horses. He nickered low but eagerly. There was no reply, but Buck saw a head move in the gloom. He nickered again, and again there was no answer.

Buck left the crack and took the beaten path around the walls, as he had so many times before. This time, however, he searched with a new determination, a new need. Before the burro had been there; now he was alone. The walls of the fence had not changed. Buck knew where the door was, having seen it open numerous times, but it was closed. He nudged it with his muzzle; it was firm and solid. The search revealed no weak spots. Stallion pens are built extra well to hold their headstrong and sometimes rebellious occupants.

Buck would not give up. He continued on, going in under the shed, and there in the gloom he discovered something he had not seen before. He stopped short. The window above the hay manger was open. The man, for the first time, had failed to close it, perhaps because he had become worried by the yellow horse's strange behavior.

The window was not large enough for a normal-sized horse to go through. Also, being above the manger, it was in a difficult place to reach. But Buck was agile and strong, and had been scrambling over boulders and downed logs and windblown tangles all his life. Then, too, he was being driven by a powerful inner torment.

The fact that the manger was practically full of hay helped. Buck got his front hoofs up in the hay; then he got them in the lower edge of the opening. He put his head through and began to climb, churning the hay with his hind legs. He got his shoulders into the opening and was unable to squeeze any farther; there was not enough room for his elbows and deep chest. He kept pushing and churning. The sharp end of a nail dug into his hide, but he gave it no attention. Gaining a little space, he threw himself against the wall. There was a snap, followed by loud cracking, and the section of wall just below the window gave way. Then there were new sharp points and splinters of wood, but none that seriously hurt him, and Buck discovered he had plenty of room, all he needed to get through.

He found himself in a dark runway, with the wall of wood on one side and a wall of stacked hay bales on the other. At one end there was a lighter opening. Buck made for it, and a second later was outside. There were scrapes on his front legs and on his flanks, and a nail cut on his chest, but he was too excited to notice them.

Now he was in a runway between two corral fences and went along at an eager trot. He came to a corner, and then another one. There was no closed gate to bar his way. Clearing the fences, he turned unerringly in the direction of the windmill.

At the water tank he went among the dark forms unhesitantly. There were several cows and a big bull, all lying down, and three horses—two mares and the suckling foal of one of them. Buck touched noses with the mares briefly, then ranged around the tank. There were no other horses. The cows did not rise. Buck went back to the mares and stood with them a short time. The restlessness in him was too deep for inaction. He nickered softly to the mares and left the tank, heading in the darkness over the packed ground on which he had seen so many horses and cows travel.

The cattle still did not stir, but the two mares followed Buck, curious about him and what he intended to do, and the foal trailed behind its mother.

17

After leaving the ranch windmill, Buck traveled steadily toward the high country. The two mares and the foal followed. They reached good grass, and the mares stopped to eat. Buck stopped, too. The grass was pleasing after the long months of eating hay. When their stomachs were full, they gathered in a little group in the prairie darkness to sleep. The foal—a filly—lay down, but the others dozed on their feet.

Dawn found them still there. The mares awoke and began to graze. Buck and the filly went along with them. They had been eating for some time, and the sun was well up in the sky when a distant dot of movement caught Buck's attention. His head went up at once, and he watched intently. The mares noticed but soon returned to grazing.

The dot became larger, and Buck soon saw there were two more. They grew steadily in size. Buck knew a short time later that they were horses, traveling straight and steadily in the manner of horses when men are on their backs. Buck snorted his irritation, and the mares lifted their heads again. Not many minutes passed before Buck could see the men clearly. About that time they put their horses to the gallop.

Buck snorted again, sent up a defiant challenge, and took a few prancing steps. The three men came on. Buck turned, ran to the nearest mare, and with sharp nips put her in motion. The other one and the filly, now somewhat excited, joined her at a fast trot.

The riders veered to the right and increased their speed. Buck knew this for what it was, an attempt to get to the front and stop or turn the mares. He ran up behind the nearest one and gave her a sharp nip with his jaws. She lengthened her stride, and the one in front entered into the spirit of the matter with a bucking, kicking burst of speed that was immediately copied by the filly. Well-bred and in good condition, the three of them skimmed over the short grass with long easy strides. Buck kept close behind.

The men were well mounted and determined. They used their spurs and quirts and made a race of it. The big mare in front of the little bunch accepted the challenge and lined out, her ears pinned back. This went on for some time, the riders gaining at first, but later beginning to lose their position. Buck saw this and was pleased, but another stiff half a mile was necessary before the men straightened in their saddles and let their weary horses ease down.

The mare up front knew the run was over and reduced her gallop to a long trot. A little later she came to a halt and turned to look back. The riders were no longer moving; they had gathered into a little knot. Buck took a long deep breath as he watched them and slowly let the air out. He, too, knew that the race was won, but experience had taught him that this did not always mean the riders were giving up. A little later he bared his teeth and switched his tail to send the two mares along. The filly trotted after them.

Some time later they came to a fence, a line of upright posts in the distance with thin, hardly visible strands of wire connecting them. The mare in front knew the country. She veered to the left, and half a mile or so farther, they came to a well-beaten trail, which she followed. Other trails joined it and led to a road, two dusty traces that wound and twisted over the rolling grassland. The mare turned onto this and continued. In time they came to the fence again. The two parallel tracks went through a gate, but the gate itself was blocked by barbed-wire strands. The mare halted and stood looking at the country beyond. Barbed wire was something she could not conquer.

Buck had had experience with barbed wire, too, and knew the barbs were sharp and could hurt. But most of the fences he had seen were drift fences, to keep loose stock within certain areas. Many such fences in the upper country were poorly repaired, and some no longer of any value for their original purposes. The range horses soon found ways around them or through them. Buck turned along the fence, and the mares followed him.

In building their fences ranchers take advantage of any natural barriers, such as bluffs, cliffs, rock piles, even a wide waterway like a river or lake. Buck saw a dark wall of rock some distance away and followed the fence toward it. When he arrived, he saw that the fence ended at the foot of the wall and was resumed on the rim above. There was not room to go between the fence and the wall, but the rock there was broken and seamed. Buck studied the wall briefly, then started to climb. First he had to find a way up and then find a way past the fence. Not only was the climb easy for him, but signs in the crevices showed it had been done before, more than once. Down on the other side, he looked back. One of the mares had followed and was now ascending in the tracks he had left. The second mare, the one with the suckling filly, was still behind the fence, lacking the courage to try the climb.

Buck struck out at a trot with the first mare—a bay—behind him. The other mare neighed indignantly at being left behind but she still would not attempt the rocks, doubtless because she had the foal with her.

Coming to tempting grass, Buck and the mare with him

stopped to graze. They ate until their stomachs were comfortable and settled themselves in the dark to sleep. During the night they were awakened by loud sounds—the hum and roaring of truck engines. Bright lights appeared and sent long widening paths over the rolling country to their right. Buck had become accustomed to these lights and engine sounds during his long months in the stallion pen, so he was not frightened. Neither was the mare. At the first light of day they began to graze. Not long afterward, horsemen appeared, and from an unexpected direction—ahead of them.

Buck's head snapped up at once, and he studied the riders carefully. As on the previous day, there were three of them. They were spread some distance apart, and came on steadily. It was a tactic Buck immediately recognized. He gave an urgent call to the mare and leaped into a gallop, in a direction parallel to the line of riders. They quickly turned their horses and rode at a hard gallop, with the intention of turning Buck back toward the ranch from which he had escaped. Buck leveled down, knowing that it was a race and that he must avoid being headed. He had two advantages—the first was not carrying any additional weight; the second was a fixed determination. The footing was good, and his hard hoofs raised a rhythmic drumming.

The mare behind, long-legged and high-withered, had the speed and stamina of her thoroughbred breeding. She stayed near Buck's heels with long smooth strides. The excitement roused her instincts to escape, even though she had been accustomed to domination and control by men.

Having moved by truck during the night, the men had put themselves and their horses in a place of advantage, ahead of Buck. Now they could, or thought they could, turn him. Once back in the vicinity of the ranch where there were fences, they were sure they could find some way to corral or capture him.

But Buck had a different idea. Up in front were the high

indistinct outlines of the sprawling Owyhees, and whether he could see them or not, some inner sense of direction told him they were there, and that was where he was going.

The first of the three runners, mounted on a strong fresh sorrel, gained some ground, enough he must have thought to achieve his purpose of getting ahead of Buck because he began to angle in. Buck saw this and called on his strong heart for more speed, hurdling the low brush now beginning to appear. The mare behind him matched easily the increase in stride. Long dormant impulses were making themselves felt inside her.

The runner was equal to the challenge. As his horse swept along he took a coiled rope from his saddle horn and shook out a loop, to be ready if the opportunity came.

Buck could see the danger. He had to bend his course away from the direct line he had been following, just slightly at first but more and more as the riders gained ground. It developed into a long exhausting race, but the stouthearted mare stuck loyally to his heels.

It began to be apparent that Buck's best was not enough. Fat from the long months in the stallion pen, he could not match the other horses in wind and stamina. Pressure on his right front forced him to a deeper turn, and he was becoming more desperate when ahead he saw a thin dark line extending across the brush. Rocks. He had seen too many not to recognize them immediately. And he knew from previous runs that horses with men on their backs did not gallop as swiftly among big boulders and jutting upthrusts. He changed his direction toward the dark line.

The men on horseback quickly realized what was happening and knew the deciding moments of the chase were at hand. They swerved their mounts to the new direction and called on them for even more speed.

The front horse of the runners, the sorrel, was a splendid

animal with courage and a long ground-eating stride. Buck had gained distance on the turn, but now this horse began to gain anew. The rider was hunched in his saddle to cut down wind resistance. Buck could hear the breaking of the brittle sage under those powerful hoofs. Just then Buck discovered that there was a horseman on his other side, up almost even with him. One of the other runners, taking advantage of the turn, too, had shortened the distance to reach this position.

With a rider now on either side, Buck knew there could be no further turning. It would be a straightaway run, stride against stride, speed against speed. Buck stretched his legs to the utmost, pushing his nose out low and level, nostrils flared wide to the wind.

The line of the rocks grew darker and taller swiftly. The horsemen on either side began to shout and yell in an effort to confuse Buck, to panic him into trying to attempt a turn. Under this pressure the good mare sprinted up until she was beside him, then dropped back until her head was near his shoulder.

Buck held staunchly to his goal. The line of boulders was not far now, nor were the riders on either side. The man on his right straightened in his stirrups and gave his rope a couple of preliminary whirls about his head, but the distance was too great, and he knew it.

The rocks loomed up before Buck, big round boulders half buried in the ground, with a broken four-foot ledge on beyond.

"Hi! Hi!" the men cried in snapping threatening tones. "Hi-i-i! Hi!"

Buck paid no attention to them. His eyes were searching the rocks ahead. They were big and close together. Then he saw an opening, a twisted path between them. It would be tricky. He had to slow down to enter. At that a sound of triumph came to the cries of the men, and both began swinging their ropes, thinking that Buck would have to come back by one or the other of them.

But Buck knew these rocks, had known them from the time he was born. He made a quick turn into the narrow opening, his hoofs throwing up a spray of fine gravel. A big round half-buried boulder was squarely in front of him with no way to get around it. Up he went boldly, his tough surefooted hoofs holding like rubber. The mare, close behind him, hesitated, but only for an instant; then she, too, was on the boulder. One foot slipped, but the other three held fast on the slanted surface. She cleared the front, gained the rounded crest, and followed the yellow stallion over it, just in time to avoid a desperately thrown loop from behind.

The leader pulled his horse up at the edge of the rocks. The big sorrel's flanks were heaving, and sweat cut tiny wet furrows through the gray dust on his sides.

The man uttered a cry of exasperation. "Dad blame it!"

"Go on," urged the one behind him. "If they can get through, we can."

"That's what you think," the first man replied. "They're unshod; they can make it, if they don't fall and break a leg. But our horses have shoes; those rocks would be just like glass under them."

The third man rode up in time to hear this. "That's right," he agreed. "I don't mind seeing the stud get away. Maybe it's just as well. It could keep the boss from making a fool of himself. But I hate to see that good mare go."

"Me, too," the first one answered. "It was a stupid idea to start with, breeding good mares to a mustang. But I don't see any sense in taking a chance of getting our legs broken in those rocks—or our necks maybe. Anyhow, the mare's branded, and there's a good chance we can get her back later. If someone catches her, they'll let us know."

The other rider nodded his head willingly and said, "That's right. She wasn't too good a mare anyway. I knew all the time it wasn't going to work. We got the one with the colt. That ought to make the boss happy. Let's head back."

18

Buck, tired and traveling at a slow walk because he knew the runners had stopped, followed along the rock ledge until he came to a littered crevice. He turned there and scrambled up to the lip. The red mare hesitated, then made the attempt. The shale rolled and slid around her bigger feet, but she kept on grimly until she too stood on the brink.

Buck looked back down the boulder-strewn slope for several minutes. Far below he could see a little group of three riders heading back to the lower country. He watched them for a while, then turned and made his way into the field of boulders that lay above the ledge. It took time to find a way through them, but neither Buck nor the mare was in a hurry. On the contrary, they were tired and hungry and stopped frequently to nibble at the good browse. The smell of water was strong at the top of a small crest, and the mare took the lead down, coming to a spring that seeped from under a huge rounded boulder. The area was trampled with tracks of antelope, deer, cattle, and other horses. A coyote slipped away like a gray shadow as they came up, and a covey of thick-bodied birds gave the mare a start by rocketing up a few feet from her nose. She quickly recovered, however, and found a little pocket of clear water where they both drank. They spent the night on the downwind side of the boulder.

In the morning Buck set out, traveling leisurely and taking

frequent bites of food. The mare followed, content with his company. Though he did not cover much ground that day, Buck kept his nose pretty generally pointed at the outline of the mountains, which was now not as faint as it had been.

This continued for three more days. Each day found the two more rested and less hungry, and they traveled more and more steadily. The ground was rocky, and the brush was brittle and thick, but Buck never permitted himself to be diverted very long from his chosen direction.

On the fourth day they came to a wide valley that ran far back up into a pocket in the side of the mountain range. Here there were fewer rocks and brush and more grass, and far down, at the mouth of the valley, Buck could see the spinning wheel of a windmill, which reminded him of the ranch where he had spent the winter. He did not watch the windmill long and did not notice the buildings and corrals clustered about it because almost as soon as they cleared the crest, his attention was caught by the sight of a small bunch of horses below in the valley. Quickly his head came up, and the mare raised her head, too.

It was a band of ranch broodmares with their suckling foals. The colts, born in late winter in foaling stalls, were now big and well nourished.

Buck let out a ringing neigh. This was just what he was looking for. That they were carefully chosen and costly mares was, of course, something he did not know, and it would have made no difference if he had. He started down the slope toward them. The bay mare followed, likewise pleased at the prospect of companions.

The spirited mares came running, led by a big black with long flowing mane and tail. Buck knew at once it was a stallion. This neither surprised nor dismayed him. It was a normal situation. He sent up a strong hoarse challenge.

The black replied. He was a magnificent beast, fully formed

with a shining coat. He was also the product of carefully selected stock, bred to sire valuable colts that the ranch owner hoped would be equally beautiful. It was only on the better days that horses such as these were let out of their stalls and paddocks to graze on the good pasture grasses. To Buck, however, they were only horses.

As they approached each other, Buck discovered there was a barrier between them, a strong plank fence like the ones at the ranch from which he had escaped. He slowed his trot. The black, on his side of the white planks, came to a halt, but continued to toss his well-shaped head and to send angry threats across at Buck.

Buck moved up to the fence. The two heads—one black, and the other yellow—touched above it, nostrils wide-blown. The two bodies were completely still, yet charged with danger and savage intent. The black was the taller and heavier, but Buck was by now a picture of lean strength and stamina.

With shrill squeals they rose into the air, flailing at each other with their forefeet, darting widespread jaws at each other's throat. Buck was quicker; his teeth found and locked on the black hide. The black came forward, his weight falling on the fence. The top board cracked and splintered; then the fall separated them. Buck kept his feet, and the black scrambled quickly up. Neither seemed to see what was left of the fence; they both hit it at the same time. The boards creaked and cracked as the two stallions sparred with their jaws above it. Buck again got hold of the black stallion's skin and gave it a merciless twist before he was knocked loose by a blow from the big dark head.

The black's lower legs became entangled in the wreckage of the fence. Buck attacked fiercely, driving the bigger horse backward and following him through the hole. Carefully reared in a stable, the black had never before experienced such savage

determination. In fact, most of his previous fighting had been in the form of blustering and threatening over paddock fences and through stable walls. Now he was feeling pain, hard driving blows and slashing cutting teeth. He wheeled about and lashed out with his heels. Buck leaped aside, drove in, and ripped a deep gash in the dark hide just back of the ribs. The heels came his way again, and he whirled out of reach.

The black crabbed backward, searching the air with his hoofs. Buck waited, picked his instant, and charged, crashing his chest full against a dark shoulder. The black went down. Buck walked over him, then turned and leaped back to get a deep grip in the mane just in front of the withers as the other stallion heaved himself up. The tangle of thick hair prevented Buck from getting a good hold. He felt the black desperately searching underneath for his forelegs and folded them backward until he could spin away. He dropped his forefeet to the ground and kicked savagely. Both hind feet landed solidly, and the black let out a grunt of pain.

The black stallion turned away from the fight; he had had enough. But in the wild bands it did not end like that. Buck pursued him, slashing at the stallion's dusty black flank with the sharp edges of his big teeth. Blood flowed into the dust. The black yelled out his pain. He limped deeply on one front leg as he tried to run. Buck was relentless, reaching for the tender flanks with cruelly twisting jaws. The black managed to break into a gallop. Buck gave him another slash as something to remember, then paused. The black went some distance away before he halted.

While the two stallions fought, the bay mare that had been with Buck went through the broken opening in the fence and sniffed at the mares there. Several put back their ears, but there was no immediate fighting. After a time Buck's mare came through the opening. The others followed her, colts and all.

Excited by the new freedom, one of them struck into a gallop. A short time later all of them were running through the low brush, with Buck coming behind. Blood trickled from a cut on his back, and there were dusty marks of heels on his sides, but otherwise he showed no effects of the recent battle.

Still farther back, the black stud, unwilling to accept total defeat, followed at a labored uneven gallop.

They cleared a corner of the fence, swung in a long curve over the grass and left the valley, a nimble-footed little brown mare running in the lead with a fat filly foal bouncing at her side. For a time they were among scattered evergreen trees and afterward broke out close to the summit of a rock-strewn ridge. Over this there was better footing and, farther down, some short but nutritious grass. The brown mare had now had her run and put down her head to eat. The others followed her example, and the foals sidled close to their mothers' flanks to suck.

Buck was hungry, too, but regularly lifted his head to gaze back up the slope. Presently in the late evening light a dark form, traveling with a limp, came into sight there. Sighting the bunch below, it halted and was still there when darkness fell. Having already established his superiority, Buck did not challenge the other stallion. As the possessor and, as he saw it, the protector of a band of mares and foals, he was fulfilling the wild stud's destiny.

The next morning the mountains loomed nearer. When the horses had grazed and the foals had nursed, Buck urged the brown mare to start in that direction. She did, apparently satisfied with the choice. The country was rougher, the valleys smaller but deeper. The brush was thicker, and the trees were more numerous, mostly cedar and juniper. There also were more rocks, boulders, and jutting ledges. Higher, there were the dark walls of the rimrock cliffs.

Near noon they watered and afterward gathered on a knoll,

where a sharp breeze discouraged the flies. There they dozed. An hour or so later Buck's attention was caught by a movement on the slope below. He was instantly alert. A horseman was there, and as Buck watched, two more came into view. They rode at a walk, not coming upward, giving no indication that they were aware of the bunch.

Buck watched silently, knowing this was not the time for a challenge. The black stallion, he noted, was nowhere to be seen, though earlier in the morning he had been following the band. The riders must have passed him.

The others were now aware of the horsemen, but the small brown mare showed no signs of nervousness. In fact, the sight of men on horseback was commonplace; she and the others had often seen them during their lives on the ranch meadows. But Buck was suspicious, keenly so. In his experience horses with men on their backs had always meant trouble.

These men, however, neither quickened their pace nor turned toward the band. They went on by. Buck continued to watch, and presently he saw that, past the position of the band, the riders were climbing in a direction that would in time put them in front, between the band and the long slopes leading to the higher ridges ahead. He stamped a front hoof on the hard ground and snorted. This brought all of them alert, the foals at once seeking their mothers.

Buck started climbing among them, his head high, obviously alarmed. The mares caught the excitement, swirling around him, and the brown mare broke out to take the lead. The others followed, responding to deep-down instincts. Soon all of them were moving at the long trot that often preceded running.

Immediately the men altered their direction still farther and put their horses at a trot, too. They were from the ranch at the mouth of the valley. Having discovered the broken fence and that the brood band was missing early that morning, they had correctly guessed what had happened and had started out to recapture the valuable mares and their young foals. Seeing the injured black stallion had not improved their tempers. One of them was the same young rider who four years earlier with his father had run Buck as a colt. Now back from his military service, he was working for the owner of a neighboring horse ranch, helping care for the broodmares and their foals.

Seeing what the riders intended, Buck began to gallop in his place behind the band. The mares in front immediately picked up the increased pace, and it spread along the line. The spirited brown accepted it willingly, and in only a few seconds a desperate race had developed.

Knowing this was a crucial time, the men put their horses to a stiff gallop. They had to get in front of the mares on the brushy bench ahead or, the rolling terrain being what it was, there would be no chance of heading them. Once the horses were into the steep rocky canyons, it would take days—maybe weeks—of additional hard riding to catch them.

Buck realized this as quickly as the men did and increased his speed. Soon he was nearly level with the tail-end mare—a white-stockinged sorrel—and her foal. The foal, frightened by Buck, spurted forward past the mare, and soon all of them were running faster.

Still Buck was not content. While having the disadvantage of climbing upward, the men were on strong capable horses that clambered over the rocks with threatening speed. Buck rushed the stocking-footed mare and gave her a sharp nip on the rump. Her leap forward started another increase in action.

On they went, on and on. The little foals ran easily, but the heavier mares were beginning to labor. The men, realizing how close it was going to be, began to spur their horses, and their mounts responded with high strong lunges. For a long instant the result hung in delicate balance, and then the riders ceased to spur and let their horses coast to a panting, sweat-dripping halt.

Buck knew almost immediately that the race was over, that he and the band had won. He welcomed the opportunity to slacken his pace, and the mares and colts in front slowed down, too. The danger no longer existed; there was no way the riders could head them now. They all knew it.

Sure of himself, Buck stopped and turned, to look back down at the horsemen. They were scattered among the rocks, and the nearest one to Buck had swung down from his horse. While Buck watched, this man went down on one knee in front of his horse, and then a shocking blow hit Buck somewhere up on his neck, and knocked him flat. As he fell, he vaguely heard the echoing of a loud explosive sound, and his last fleeting impression as he went down on the steep shale slope was of the mares stampeding away in a new wave of startled fright.

19

Consciousness returned to Buck slowly. The sun was bright and high in the sky.

The man had not made as good a shot as he had thought. He had intended to kill the yellow stallion, believing that to be the only way he could get his prized mares and foals back. Also he was still angry about the injuries to the highly bred black stallion. But luckily for Buck, the bullet had gone high, into his dark mane, and passing through, had merely nicked one of the vertebrae of his backbone. Had it been an inch or so lower, Buck would never have regained consciousness. That had been the fate of many range studs, and many ranchers considered it good riddance.

Buck lay still, not sure he should try to move or even if he could. There was a great strange weakness in him, and the world all about was silent and still. A little later he was aware of the soft buzzing of insects flying about his head, and tried to prick his ears to discourage them. This seemed to reestablish the connection between his mind and his body. He knew something was wrong, that some kind of emergency existed, but when he tried to raise his head, he found he was too weak to do so. It was only by great determination and effort that he could make any movement at all. He let his head sink back to the ground and was content just to rest for a time. Nothing, it seemed, could be important enough to justify the tremendous concentration and effort needed to move his legs.

He drifted off briefly and then came back to reality, and was conscious of the sunlight and of the shattered shale beneath his ribs. There was no sound, and the strongest smell was of heat and dry dust. High above in the blue there was a slowly circling dot that he knew to be a bird. To lift his head was a big effort, but he managed it and looked about. He saw nothing, no movement, and remembered the mares and foals that had been there. They were not where he had seen them last, nor were the men, either; at least they were not where he could see them, but then for some reason he could not see very well.

Sometime later his mind became clearer, and he knew he should do something; it was dangerous to stay there on the ground without knowing what was going on around him. He needed to be ready to run, so again he tried to get up, but his legs seemed to be disconnected from the rest of him. He discovered he was lying on an incline with his legs facing uphill. That made it more difficult. He was also beginning to notice a pressure in his chest, on his heart and lungs. This was a result of the forward weight of his stomach and intestines. Horses are not made to lie on their backs and in such a position will almost invariably die, sometimes in as short a period as twenty minutes. Buck, of course, did not know this, but the lack of breath in his lungs began to create a desperation inside him. He made an effort to roll over, to get his legs downhill, and found he was wedged between the slope, a small boulder, and a stunted bush.

He had to rest and did so, lying still for a few seconds while trying to regain his breath. But the pressure on his lungs increased and he knew he had to do something to relieve it, and soon. He flung his feet and legs into the air, at the same time trying to twist his body. This did not help; instead it seemed to wedge him even tighter against the boulder and brush. He made a desperate effort to gasp in air through his opened mouth, but his lungs could not receive it. He let out a little cry of panic.

Then something strange happened. There were outside forces at work, first about his head and next on his feet and legs. "We've got to get you up from there," a voice said.

There were small concussions, the movement of hoofs, in the shale around Buck. Sounds became heavy and straining, and a few seconds later the boulder was pulled from under his back. It loosened, then rolled away. There were hands on Buck's forelegs, pulling. "Come on. Come on. Turn over," the voice said.

Buck felt his body roll over the bush. His feet and legs came back to the earth downhill, and the great pressure on his heart and lungs slid away. He could breathe again. The smothering weight was gone.

"That's it," the voice said. "Take it easy. You'll be all right now."

Buck did not understand the words but he followed the instructions, pulling great gulps of the life-giving air through his mouth and nostrils.

"I knew it was you when I saw you running with the mares," the voice went on. "I didn't know he was going to shoot. . . . it wouldn't have made any difference anyway. You went down like you were shot dead. The mares stampeded and we had to go after them . . . they might have scattered all over the country. When we got them headed for the ranch, I came back . . . to see for sure. It's a good thing too. . . . you wouldn't have lasted much longer, not on your back like that."

Buck flounced in an attempt to get up and felt hands on his head, holding him down.

"You've been on my mind since that first time when Dad roped your mammy and she came over backward and broke her neck. That was a real tough break for a little guy like you. We looked all around and couldn't find you anywhere. Where'd you go to?"

Buck felt a rope being fashioned into a halter about his head and flounced again. "Whoa, whoa, fellow . . . I didn't figure you could make it, not as young as you were. But I'm glad you did. I figured we owed you something, even if you were just a mustang. Whoa! Take it easy till I get this halter on. Now"—footsteps moved away rapidly before the voice went on—"you can give it a try."

Buck realized his head was free and lunged to his feet. A few feet away the man was sitting in the saddle of a strong-bodied bay horse. "Now don't get in a lather," he said. "I'm not going to hurt you. Don't worry."

But Buck was already scrambling away, going at full tilt. Something hit him across the nose with a force that stopped him short. His rear end flew around, and he found himself looking back at the man on the horse. Now there was something he had not noticed before. A rope was stretched hard and tight from the bay's saddle horn, and the other end of it seemed to be looped around Buck's own neck just back of his ears. It held him, kept him from going any farther.

"It's all right, fellow," the man said. "Take it easy. Nobody's going to hurt you. You just need a little help; that's all."

Buck was dizzy from weakness and eased his pull on the rope a little.

"That's right," the man approved in a low tone, leaning his forearm comfortably on the top of the saddle's big horn. "The big thing is you're still alive. That's what counts. But you're not in very good shape. You've lost a lot of blood."

Buck pulled back against the rope, putting his entire weight on it. The bullet wound in his neck had started bleeding again, and a dark splotch was spreading down under his thick mane.

The man saw this and paused several seconds before saying,

"You're going to have to have some help, there's no doubt about that, or you'll be liable not to make it. There's an old cow camp over this ridge, not too far from here. It doesn't amount to a whole lot but is not a bad place. There's a good little corral with a shed and a pretty good stack of hay . . . or was the last I saw it, which was not too far back. Something'll have to be done about that hole . . . and you could stand some rest and good feed, too."

He lifted his reins and pulled the rope stretched between the two horses tighter. "Guess it's up to you and me, Barney. They can get those mares back to the ranch without us. Come on," he went on to Buck. "Don't pull back; it won't do you any good. If you'll just cooperate a little, yellow horse, we ought to get there about dark, maybe a little before. You can have a couple of forks of good sweet meadow hay for your supper, and maybe a bucket of grain, too, if it's not all gone. It'll do you good. Come on, now."

Buck hated ropes and did not want to go, but was too weak and sick to make much of a fight of it when the stout bay put his weight on the rope. Soon he learned he could save himself a lot of pain by going along willingly. The man kept talking to him, too, in low soothing tones: "You're a good little horse. I figured you could make a real good cowhorse, one a man could get things done on. You've had some sure enough tough luck, but I still think so. You ought to have a chance, which is something wild horses don't get much. Not enough grass to go around anymore."

After the first half a mile or so, Buck settled down, and they made steady progress up the slope and down through the thickets of juniper and quaking asp on the opposite side. The country, different from the rolling lower stretches of cheat grass and scrubby brush, was more like that which Buck was accustomed to. And the timber-crested outline of the mountain range was now nearer and seemed higher. The rich smells, the occasional rattle of broken rock beneath his hoofs, and the soft touch of the changing breeze all brought a feeling of inner comfort to the yellow stallion.

The stars were beginning to make themselves visible when the bay came to a small fenced meadow and halted before a strong round-rail gate. "Here we are," the man said cheerfully. "Not a bad spot, either, if you don't mind being alone." He leaned forward to open the gate without dismounting and rode through. Buck had a distrust of gates but, when the pressure came behind his ears, he was too weary to do anything other than follow the other horse. The man turned back briefly and closed the gate with easy familiarity.

A short distance farther on they came to a small corral. "This is it," the man told Buck. His voice had the tone of one used to speaking to animals; in fact, he had spent most of his life with them. "It may not look like much to you," he continued, "but to Barney and me, it's a lot like home. It ought to be, from the time we've spent up here. We're in luck, too. The deer and elk haven't busted through to the hay yet."

It was a cow camp, a sort of a summer outpost of the ranch for which the young man worked. Since it might be used anytime by riders who were in the vicinity, it was kept supplied with food and feed. There was a small and weathered log cabin not far away.

The man dismounted, untied Buck's rope from the saddle horn and tried to lead Buck through the corral gate. Buck set his legs stubbornly and would not go. The man hesitated and said, "All right, if that's the way you have to have it." He swung back up on the bay, gave the rope a couple of twists about the worn horn, and spoke to his horse. The tightening of the rope brought Buck forward at once.

Inside the corral, the man dismounted again, untied the rope, and let the end drop to the ground. He then took the saddle and bridle from the bay and went back through the gate, closing it behind him.

The bay moved at once to a corner of the small enclosure where there was the trickling sound of water. Buck was thirsty, too, but he stubbornly refused to drink. The man came back and threw hay into a manger under the shed. The bay was there already, waiting in the gloom for it.

Still Buck did not move.

The man threw in another fork of hay and waited. After a few seconds he spoke, "Don't be like that. What's the use making it so tough on yourself? Barney, don't you make a pig of yourself." He left the corral and went to the cabin.

The next morning he came back to the corral early and stood for some time looking through the opening between the top rails. Barney's bay flanks were comfortably full. There was still hay left in the manger. Buck stood in the soft dust with a gaunt forlorn appearance.

The man had not yet put on his big hat, and the wrinkles of a frown appeared on his forehead. "You ought to have more sense than that," he said presently. A little later he added, "Maybe you're hurt worse than I think. I guess I'll have to do something about that."

He left and was soon back, carrying an old bucket half-full of a dark liquid. Barney came to him immediately and extended his nose. "Back," the man said. "This is the dope bucket; you can't eat it. Let it alone now." He put the bucket under a bottom rail where it would be safe, then approached Buck, stooped, and picked up the end of the halter rope.

Even though the pressure on the sore area of his neck was slight at the time, Buck reacted as if he had been suddenly attacked by a swarm of hornets. He leaped into the air, striking and kicking. Surprised, the man dodged aside but was too late to avoid Buck's shoulder. The blow knocked him spinning, and he went down into the dust. Almost instantly, however, he was back on his feet. With the rope still in his hands he braced his booted feet, and was literally jerked into the air when Buck hit the end of rope. The man went down again, the rope burning the palms

127

of his hands. He let it go, sat up, and looked at them unhappily.

Buck went on, hit the fence blindly. The tough juniper rails threw him back on his haunches. He lunged forward and hit another place. This, too, held firmly. Buck ran on around the little corral, wildly looking for a place he could go.

The man got to his feet. "You crazy fool! Quit that!" Buck kept going, bucking and kicking and slinging his head about. Dust flew up from his feet. A raucous grunt, half a moan, came from his downheld throat.

The man darted forward. The rope was slithering through the dust like a long thin snake. The man ducked down, grabbed it, and carefully watching his chance, threw a loop of the rope over the high end of one of the fence posts, then braced himself. The subsequent jerk was another shock to the palms of his hands but he held on grimly. At the end of the lariat Buck was jerked high, and went over backward into the dust. He was up quickly and came jumping back along the fence. The man staggered backward, taking up the slack from the rope as swiftly as he could around the post.

Buck went past, kicking up a cloud of dust. The man could see the jolt coming and braced his long legs for it. Buck slammed first into the length of rope stretched between the fence and the man, and then hit the end of the short section left to him. The old juniper post creaked and shuddered in its solid mooring in the packed earth, but it held. The man fought for his end of the rope until he got it free from the horse's flailing legs and ran back to make a lightning tie about the top of a neighboring post.

Buck was lying on his side in the dust, his nose held up by the rope around the post. He struggled briefly, trying to find room to get up, but his legs were tangled in the lower rails.

"Whoa! Whoa!" the man said exasperatedly. "You'll knock your brains out. Haven't you got any sense?"

Buck became still, more from exhaustion than anything else.

"There. That's better. Hang on. This'll take only a minute."

The man went to the fence and got the dope bucket. It had a stick in it, with a rag tied at the bottom to make a swab. Back at Buck's side, he pulled the festering scab from the bullet wound. This sent Buck into another frenzy of struggling. The man picked up the bucket and moved back, away from the danger of those flying hoofs. "You crazy nut! That's the trouble with you wild ones; you don't know when to quit. I'm just trying to help you. Whoa! Be still!"

Buck was exhausted again. With his feet in the rails and his head held up, nose first, by the rope, he was in a helpless position. The man approached him again, knelt by his neck, and in a single quick jerk, yanked the scab free. Buck flinched. "All right, I know it hurt, but it's got to be done, or it won't get well at all." He lifted the dripping swab from the bucket and put it against the wound. Buck's nostrils were quivering with his heavy breathing, but otherwise he did not move. The man saturated the wound thoroughly with the dark liquid; then he went around through the gate, and reaching between the lower rails, did the same thing to the hole on the other side of Buck's neck. Buck still did not move.

The man took his time. After he had finished, he put the bucket back out of the way, untied the rope from the second post and let the slack play around the one above Buck's head. Buck's nose went back to the ground, and his breathing became easier, but otherwise he did not seem to notice. The man remained outside the fence. "OK, you're loose," he said. "Get up. Go ahead, you're not tied."

Buck stayed as he was, his eyes half closed and his yellow body dulled by a film of dust. The man caught one of Buck's front feet and pushed it back through the fence crack. "Go on, get up," he ordered, exasperated still more. "What's the matter with you?" He pushed the toe of his boot through the crack in the fence and gave Buck a dig in the flank. The horse gave no indication that he felt it. The man drove the toe forward still more vigorously with the same result. His eyes became thoughtful, and he said, "What's the matter with you? You can't be hurt that bad."

Buck was vaguely aware of all this, but he did not care. His whole body ached, and he knew he was helpless, defeated. He no longer cared about anything. All he wanted to do was just to lie there, and hope no one would bother or hurt him.

The man was still standing at the fence, a perplexed and unhappy look in his eyes, when a voice from behind asked, "Problem?"

The young man whirled quickly and saw an older man standing a few steps back. On beyond this newcomer, near the old cabin, a saddled roan was standing quietly to a single rein wrapped about the warped old hitchrail.

"Oh, Dad . . . " the young rider exclaimed. "Where'd you come from? How'd you know I was up here?"

"Figured you could be. Ran into the fellows with the mares late yesterday. They were headed back to the ranch. They told me what had happened, that you had come back to check on the stallion. I got a real early start this morning, and kept old Roanie moving. Couldn't find either one of you but saw your tracks."

"The shot didn't kill him," the son said.

"I guessed that."

"Came awful close though. Knocked him flat. Hit him high on the neck."

The father nodded. "Creased him, we used to call it. That was one way of catching the real wild ones, if you could get to them soon enough, before they came to again. It killed a lot more than it caught though."

The son said, "He piled up against a boulder downhill on his back. He couldn't turn over, and he couldn't get up. He was almost gone when I got to him. Sure glad I came back."

"You've always had a weakness for him," the father answered, smiling.

"Yes. He's a nice little stud. I figured he needed some time before doing a lot of traveling, so I decided to bring him up here. But," he went on, his brow furrowing, "he acts a little funny. Just quits. Like now. I had to throw him to doctor the wound in his neck, and he won't get up. Just lies there."

The man, now leaning on the fence rail beside his son, turned his attention to Buck, his eyes sharp and questioning. "What's the matter, little stud?" he asked gently. He put the toe of his boot through and gave the horse a prod.

"It doesn't make sense," the younger man said. "He's not in that bad shape. Only a little while ago he was fighting like a wildcat, tried to run right over me. Now he won't even get up."

The father did not answer for a minute or more, during which he kept his shrewd gaze fixed on the downed horse. "It could be he's one of them that just can't take it," he said slowly, "the kind that will go over a cliff, if there's one handy. They are throwbacks to the old days when horses went for years—maybe two or three generations—without ever being caught. The instinct for freedom is powerfully strong in them."

"I can handle him," the son replied. "I can break him to ride."

The father still spoke slowly, choosing his words. "Yes, you can. You can handle him all right. It wouldn't be easy . . . you'd have to put a lot of rope on him, just like a little while ago. Like there is now. But I don't know whether you'd have much, whether it'd be worth the trouble or not."

"Why not? He's strong and tough. He's been raised up here in these hills. He could go all day with a man on his back. His colts ought to be strong and tough, too, if we decided to use him as a sire."

The man rubbed his chin thoughtfully. "I don't know.

Maybe—and maybe not. When it's there, the trait can be mighty strong. It seems like they just don't have any control over it. Sure you can break 'em, someone like you, who knows how. You can stop 'em from fighting; you can get 'em so they'll stand to be caught—in a corral. But can you make 'em like it? Can you do it without breaking their spirit, too? It used to happen regularly, especially with stallions who had had bands and were this old. I saw it more than once. Their instinct for freedom just won't die, not as long as there is anything else left."

The son hesitated. "You think he's one . . . like that?"

After a silence that ended in a somewhat regretful shrug, the father said, "Look at him. What's keeping him from getting up? He knows he can; he knows the rope is slack. He could be on his feet in half a second—sometimes they won't even eat, just starve their hearts out. . . ." He left the rest of what he might have said hanging in the silence.

The younger man said, "What about it? What can be done? There must be something. . . ."

"Not much, far as I know." The man rubbed his grizzled chin. "No good answer. The canners will take him. . . . they'll take anything with meat and hide on its bones, as you know. They will even pay enough to make it worthwhile hauling him out to the saleyard. Chickens have to eat, too." He paused before going on. "The easiest way would be another bullet, lower down. It would be the quickest, too. A lot of ranchers wouldn't hesitate to pull the trigger. It'd save trouble and leave grass for other horses . . . for cattle, too. Beef is worth good money. Also, I figure if he had his choice he would probably take that before the slaughterhouse. Wouldn't you?"

The son shook his head, as if trying to get a disagreeable thought out of his mind. His gaze lowered to the yellow shape lying near the fence. "No," he said. "No," he repeated, briefly but definitely. "Why not take off the rope and open the gate?

His old range is not too awful far from here. He'd make it back there pretty quick, wouldn't he?"

"That's another way . . . easy one, too," the older man said. "It might work . . . and it might be you wouldn't be doing him much of a favor."

"What do you mean? He knows the country. That's his home. That's where we saw him the first time."

"True enough. But he has lost a lot of blood; he's pretty weak. The first bunch he ran across . . . there would be a fight, almost a cinch. He's that kind; fighting is his life, born in him. He knows what it is to have his own bunch . . . but he'd likely lose, the shape he's in. The other stud would beat him up, maybe even kill him. It's happened; you've seen the old skeletons up there. I don't think he'd have much of a chance."

The son thought that over and could find no reply.

After a silence the father went on, his voice soft and understanding, "I know how you feel about this stud, even before you went into the army. I like him, too, and I am sure not eager for the job . . . but if you'd like for me to handle it. . . . I brought my rifle along, thought I might have a chance for some fresh venison up here. We can use the meat."

The younger man shook his head. "No," he said; and a second later he repeated it in a voice that showed his mind was made up even more firmly now, "No! I've seen enough of killing. There's quite a bit of hay left here, and some grain. They can get along without me at Burlman's for . . . for as long as it takes. I figure that with good feed and care, it won't take too long. He ought to get his strength back fast, and his pep. I'll need to doctor that neck a few more times, too. It was getting some infection."

The father's answer was easy and pleased. "No, it shouldn't take too long. On my way home I'll swing by Burlman's place and tell them you found some real important business up here and will be delayed a while. I am sure they'll understand. Don't worry about it, son." There was quiet pride in the way he said it.

They went inside the corral and, moving carefully, got the rope off Buck. He gave no sign that he knew it had been removed. The men went through the gate, closed it behind them, and a short time later the older man got on the roan gelding and rode away.

With a couple of more treatments to his neck injury, plenty of good feed, and the bay, Barney, for company, Buck soon began to improve. His eyes brightened, his wound healed, and as the nights turned colder, his yellow coat thickened and darkened. On the soft footing, his hoofs grew longer. He began to stand for long intervals with his ears pricked up, listening it seemed to sounds or calls too distant and fragile for human ears. Afterward he would pace the corral fence, from corner to corner and back again, as restless as a caged wolf.

Noticing all this, the young man nodded happily to himself, and the worry wrinkles disappeared from his brow. One brisk morning with a strong feeling of winter in the air, he came to the corral, took a good look at Buck, and then put the bridle he carried on Barney. "Can't take a chance on your going, too. You're no wild stud, and I'm glad you're not," he said to the bay, opened the gate, and led him outside.

Buck knew quickly there was something strange, something unusual, but it took a few seconds for him to discover what it was. The corral gate was open, left that way by the man for the first time. Buck's ears whipped forward, and his eyes rolled from side to side. The man was not at the gate, nor near it. He was at the hitchrail in front of the old cabin, placing a well-worn saddle on Barney's short strong back.

Buck took a step forward, paused, then took another. Nothing happened. The man did not come running, shouting, and

swinging a long rope. Buck continued on to the gate, hesitated again, then stepped through.

The man at the cabin had stopped his saddling and was watching across Barney's back. Buck angled away, avoiding the house, and knew then for certain he was free. But he did not run; he merely walked, something telling him that for this once there was no need for wild flight. He walked on, holding himself in check, now completely under control. Reaching the top of the short rise, he halted and turned for a backward look. The man was still standing beside Barney, and as Buck watched, he lifted a hand in happy approval.

Buck went on, found the meadow gate open. Then he did run, skimming through the brush and over the rocks, headed for the high rugged country where he knew the wild bunches would be roaming.

About the Author

Glenn Balch has been writing about horses and the West for many years. Born and raised in Texas, he started to ride soon after he started to walk. His mounts have ranged from Texas cow ponies to blooded thoroughbreds and Arabians. He has ridden on west Texas cattle roundups, on Idaho mountain trails, on cavalry-drill fields and marches, in the helter-skelter excitement of polo, and even, during World War II, on jungle trails in Burma.

Mr. Balch now lives in Meridian, Idaho.

About the Artist

Ruth Sanderson, who has always been fond of horses, can remember drawing them ever since she was in the first grade. She has been the owner and rider of many horses, and has raised and trained a quarter horse as well. She particularly enjoyed illustrating this book, as she has a special interest in the subject. She recognizes the fact that to western ranchers cattle and wild horses are in competition against each other for food, but she believes a compromise can be found and that the mustangs have just as much right to life as do the cattle.

Born in Massachusetts, Ruth Sanderson was graduated in 1974 from the Paier School of Art with a commendation as an outstanding illustration student. Since then, she has illustrated a number of books that amply bear out this verdict. She now lives in Bethany, Connecticut.